No. 6 in the Harness ries

Series Editor
Michael Rigby

Information for Managing Healthcare Resources

Sheila Bullas and Dallas Ariotti

Radcliffe Medical Press

Radcliffe Medical Press Ltd
18 Marcham Road
Abingdon
Oxon OX14 1AA
United Kingdom

www.radcliffe-oxford.com
The Radcliffe Medical Press electronic catalogue and online ordering facility.
Direct sales to anywhere in the world.

British Library Cataloguing in Publication Data

A catalogue record for this book is available from the British Library.

ISBN 1 85775 474 3

Typeset by Joshua Associates Ltd, Oxford
Printed and bound by TJ International Ltd, Padstow, Cornwall

Contents

Series Editor's Preface vii

About the authors ix

1   Introduction 1

2   The workforce 17

3   Managing the estate and supplies 37

4   Managing finance to maximise health gain 61

5   Managing quality and cost 85

6   Managing processes and change 127

7   Performance management and performance review 145

8   Making it happen 167

Bibliography 173

Appendix 1 Business case 177

Appendix 2 Clinical outcome indicators 181

Appendix 3 Electronic patient records 183

Index 185

Series Editor's Preface

Information for Managing Healthcare Resources

Provision and management of healthcare resources can be a major zone of conflict and tension, due to the constant striving to provide the best possible healthcare. It is a truism to point out the vital role of human resources, the estate and other physical resources, and consumables, in successfully delivering healthcare. Finance does not itself deliver healthcare, but is the essential means of mobilising and motivating the other resource providers.

Together, these expensive and scarce resource commodities provide the means by which the health professional functions. In turn, the manager is charged with ensuring that the resources are appropriately marshalled and utilised. The way in which the resources are assembled and applied is crucial in determining the quality of care delivered, and the efficiency and effectiveness which determine not only the benefit to the individual patient, but also the total amount of care which can be delivered.

Because of this essential and well-intentioned professional and managerial self-interest, there is frequent scope for conflict over the appropriateness and use of healthcare resources. Too often what is missing is a full factual appreciation of all the aspects of resource requirements and their management.

Sheila Bullas and Dallas Ariotti have written *Information for Managing Healthcare Resources* in order to encourage objectivity and empiricism in this area. The book has been written in a systematic way by two authors with significant experience both nationally and in the practical world of the NHS. They address each of the principal resources in healthcare in turn, and identify the information available about each resource, together with details of the definitions and analyses most commonly used. They then move on to look at the organisational and other management techniques involved in optimal management of these resources.

The arena of healthcare resources has been the subject of a range of specific initiatives, such as clinical budgeting and the erstwhile Resource Management Initiative. These innovations gave a focus to the importance of managing resources, yet at the same time tended to divert attention towards short-term change. By standing back and looking at the subject more comprehensively, the authors of this book are able to refer to and highlight the strengths of the individual approaches, and at the same time package them together into a more comprehensive and enduring understanding.

The text is intended to be of equal benefit in helping professionals to understand the nature of healthcare resources and their management, and in enabling managers and policy makers to perceive objectively the requirements for and potential outputs of these resources. Both of the authors have put a considerable amount of work into bringing this text alive, with an abundance of references and many illustrations through practical examples. It is hoped that not only the reader, but also the populations served by their healthcare communities, will benefit from the knowledge gleaned from *Information for Managing Healthcare Resources*.

Michael Rigby
July 2002

About the authors

Sheila Bullas BSc(Hons), MBA started her NHS career as a student in medical laboratory technology. She completed a degree in biology at Sussex University, specialising in molecular and mathematical biology, and then worked at Shell Research Laboratories. She subsequently returned to the NHS and worked in capital and service planning, information services and computing, heading up the design, development and implementation of a successful child health system.

From 1981 she was leading systems developments for a health authority and heading an innovative office systems programme. She was seconded to the NHS Executive Resource Management Unit. This programme introduced the Clinical Directorate Structure into the NHS, with supporting information on activity and costing.

In 1991 she founded Health Strategies, an independent management and technology consultancy company working in the health-care sector, where she specialises in business strategies and complex, innovative projects integrating processes, people and information to improve health outcomes. This has provided opportunities to contribute to innovative projects currently being undertaken in the UK, and to work throughout Europe and the rest of the world.

She is also a Research Fellow of King Alfred's College, Winchester.

Dallas Ariotti BA(Hons), MPsych, SRA has worked in health systems for many years, first as a nurse and psychologist, and then as a university-based statistician with a special interest in measurement mathematics.

From 1989 to 1997 in Australia, as Principal Policy Adviser to a number of health ministers and as First Assistant Secretary in the Federal Department of Health, her responsibilities included the national policy and financing of hospital operations and private health insurance, and the National Casemix Program which built the Diagnosis Related Group (DRG) classification and payment systems for Australian hospitals. From 1995 to 1997 she was also the Secretary of the National Health and Medical Research Council.

For the past 13 years she has worked internationally with the Organisation for Economic Co-operation and Development

(OECD) on the statistics of health reforms, with the World Health Organization (WHO) on innovative research methodologies, and with the UK, New Zealand, Singapore and US Federal Governments on health system reform, including innovative financing and information strategies.

She has lived in the UK since 1999, and is currently the Director of Performance and Information Management at Guy's and St Thomas's Hospitals.

1 Introduction

Management information and management action

In the environment of unprecedented change that is the NHS at present, the current experiential approach to management decision making is not adequate to achieve the levels of performance that are demanded. An approach that is based on seeking and using the best available evidence is needed, and that is the subject of this book. We shall explore the use of information to support management decisions for the deployment and use of resources by healthcare organisations. We shall aim to demonstrate that readily available information can more than adequately support decisions on the management of healthcare resources. While researching this book, more than one clinician suggested that 'evidence-based management' was an oxymoron. We hope to prove them wrong. However, it does suggest that the culture of healthcare organisations does not always value an evidence-based approach. This is echoed in the report of an expert group on learning from adverse events in the NHS, chaired by the Chief Medical Officer, which concluded that 'the NHS culture is not – by and large – one which encourages reporting and analysis'.[1]

Effective influence on the management of resources lies not so much with senior policy makers as with operational staff who use and deploy the resources of the health sector. The purpose of information is to promote understanding and influence behaviour and decisions. Information is therefore an integral part of the culture of the organisation. We consider information use in relation to culture: its role in promoting desired behaviours, discouraging undesired behaviours and supporting change. The clear common thread is for quality information to fuel and support processes in the management of resources, and for the staff involved to be aware of the need for appropriate information, and to understand how to use it effectively.

Healthcare is operating in a rapidly changing environment, and no book can hope to be entirely up to date on the policy and practice of managing resources. What we can do is put current policy and practice into context, discuss the underlying principles that are relatively stable, and provide pointers to where up-to-date policy and practice can be found. In essence, we aim to provide a firm foundation on which readers can build in the light of future changes.

We aim to identify the sources of data on which hard information is based. We examine how the hard information, the facts and figures, are used in conjunction with soft information to form the explicit knowledge within the organisation. We look at how that explicit knowledge is used in conjunction with the tacit knowledge to inform decision making and influence the way in which the organisation functions.

It is a strange misconception that when one talks to clinicians in particular about 'managing resources', there is an automatic assumption that we are talking about the management of capital and revenue funds. Perhaps this view is enhanced by the fact that the role of 'Director of Finance' has been renamed in some UK healthcare organisations as 'Director of Resources'. We take a wider view of resources, looking at staff, facilities and time as well as money.

This book, which is part of the Harnessing Health Information series, aims to address the needs of health staff, including clinicians, managers and information staff. It aims to give explanations that are clear, reliable, authoritative and above all pragmatic. It explains current developments for those with no prior specialist knowledge and where appropriate, it aims to put these in an historical context. It gives practical examples using information that is readily available.

Managers must be able to justify their decisions and be accountable for them, just as clinicians must be accountable for their decisions. This requires that management be evidence based.[2] There is a commonality of interest in providing and accessing evidence at the level of professional development. Management functions that must be evidence based to be ethical and effective include strategic and operational management, resource management and deployment, and service development.[3] One of the problems is the paucity of published peer-reviewed management analyses, but this does not absolve managers from making the best use of the information that exists both within and outside the organisation. The same principles of evidence appraisal are appropriate as for those clinical decisions.[4]

The rest of this chapter investigates management decision making and the role that information plays as an integral part of that process. In the following chapters we shall look at the individual resources of the workforce, the estate and supplies and finance. Subsequent chapters bring these together in the integrated processes that lead to effective deployment and management of resources. Business planning, management budgeting, performance review and management, process review and change management are just some of the processes that are discussed. Information is a key part of all of these processes.

Managing resources is such a wide area that this book cannot hope to cover the full scope of the subject in any great detail. We have tried to cover the important theories in all of the main resource areas, and to consider information requirements at a high level. Examples are included, some of which you may be able to apply in your situation, while others may spark off new ideas.

The environment in which healthcare operates

Healthcare organisations are large and complex. There are many powerful and influential stakeholders with different expectations of healthcare and different goals. Figure 1.1 shows some of them. Everyone is a stakeholder in healthcare.

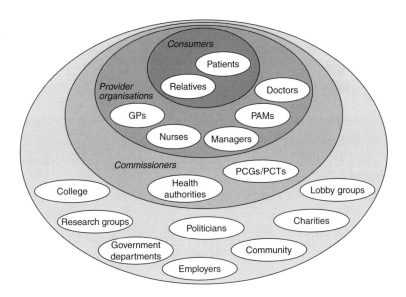

Figure 1.1 Stakeholders.

The organisations exist in a rapidly changing environment, in which the aged population, that requires the most healthcare services, is increasing more than other age groups, while the population of working age represents an increasingly smaller proportion.[5] This means more patients and clients and fewer people to care for them. Technological developments (e.g. in imaging, medical and surgical equipment and medications) are also increasing at an unprecedented rate, making it possible to provide more and more expensive treatments.

In addition, people's expectations are increasing as they have access to more and more information. Intelligent and articulate patients can become as expert (or more so) on their specific problems as the doctors who treat them. The more articulate and informed may attract a disproportionate share of healthcare resources because of their ability to exert moral and political pressure. This puts pressure on the healthcare system to ensure that resources are distributed fairly, based on priorities defined by society and clinical need, and not disproportionately to politically active and well-informed sectors. Single-issue groups as well as individuals are well positioned to apply pressure.

Political pressures are increasing, with healthcare being one of the main areas perceived as attracting votes. Emotive issues are just as likely to be the subject of targets as a more logical and rational targeting of scarce resources. Health is one of the top three pressure areas on Government, the others being employment and the economy.

Some of the pressures that have an impact on resource decisions are summarised in Figure 1.2. In the UK, these pressures must be accommodated within a cash-limited service provision. The decision with regard to what that cash limit is has more to do with what politicians perceive taxpayers are prepared to pay, and the proportion of the gross domestic product that the Treasury is prepared to spend on healthcare. Rationing is inevitable. Some of the information-based approaches to rationing are described in Chapter 4.

Healthcare is a complex environment within which resources are deployed and within which they must be managed in order to meet the goals of the diverse stakeholders. It is hardly surprising that politics plays a large part in the decisions that are made about how those resources are deployed – ruled mainly by the heart. There is also a logical rational element to that decision making – ruled mainly by the head (*see* Figure 1.3). Both sides bring hard and soft

Figure 1.2 Forces influencing resource decisions.

information to bear on their decisions. This book deals mainly with the rational, logical arguments supported by hard information, but it is always important to remember that the political social arguments are equally important in the management of resources, particularly when addressing the more complex issues. The aim is to achieve an appropriate balance.

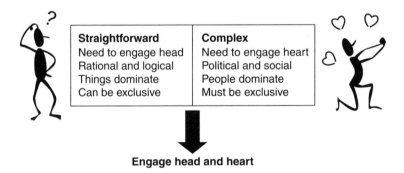

Figure 1.3 Rational vs. political.

Information: an integral part of management processes

Making relevant, accurate, timely information readily available to managers is not sufficient to ensure that it will be used to support decision making. Information needs to be understood and made an integral part of management processes, just as it is for operational processes. Defined processes, standards and templates linking information to process will help to ensure that the information used is consistent throughout the organisation.

Information itself is inherently neutral, but its application removes that neutrality – it is a source of power used by individuals and groups to enhance their influence within an organisation. Whenever a report is written or a case made, selective information is presented in support of the argument being made. When the information that needs to be presented is defined as part of management processes, there is less opportunity to leave out important factors and present a biased argument.

Example 1.1 Committing project resources

A large acute teaching hospital was developing a business case for the procurement and implementation of an *electronic patient record* (EPR). This was a multi-million-pound project that would secure a contract for provision of information systems for ten years. The EPR included complex images generated in the radiology department. These images needed to be stored in the patient record, distributed to clinicians around the hospital and manipulated to support decisions regarding the clinical care of patients.

The hospital's communication network needed major enhancements so that the images could be transmitted with sufficient speed to meet the requirements of the clinicians. Inclusion of these enhancements in the business case for the EPR meant that the affordability targets for the project could not be met.

The project team had to consider two courses of action:
- including the communications enhancements in the business case and seeking to change the affordability targets set by the Trust Board
- excluding the communications enhancements, which would then be considered as a 'must-do' project after the contract for the EPR had been agreed.

Of course, the only course of action to choose is the first one – or is it? There are many projects where major elements that make a project workable have been excluded, either intentionally or otherwise.

Information has a major role to play in the deployment and subsequent use of resources:

- in the deployment of resources, including additional resources and reallocation of existing resources, to achieve local and national targets and priorities for development
- ensuring that deployed resources are used optimally – that is, optimal performance is achieved against the criteria of health improvement, fair access, health outcomes, effective delivery of appropriate healthcare, patient/carer experience and efficiency.

How does a healthcare organisation know that it is achieving optimal performance?

The deployment of additional resources and the reallocation of existing resources can be addressed in a *business planning process* whereby a case is made that outlines the costs and benefits of a specific investment in relation to the targets and priorities set.

Ensuring that resources are used optimally is an ongoing part of a number of processes, including the following:

- *clinical governance* and *clinical audit* to monitor the effectiveness of clinical processes and outcomes
- *performance monitoring and review* to monitor how the organisation performs against the performance criteria and against standards and targets set within and outwith the organisation, and in comparison with clinical and organisational outcomes in comparable settings elsewhere
- *management budgeting* to monitor expenditure against financial allocations and agreed activity levels.

Information is an essential element in all of these processes if the organisation is to *know* whether the resources available to it are being used in the 'best' way. Information, its nature and the way in which it is used within a management process, is also essential for encouraging (or 'incentivising') the desired behaviour of individuals operating those processes.

Information for managing patient waits is a good example of information influencing behaviour. The management of patients is very different depending on whether the organisation is pursuing a target of reducing waiting-lists or waiting-time.

Although information is normally taken into account when designing new processes (e.g. development of performance management and clinical governance being designed currently), this is often as an add-on requirement rather than as a part of process design. However, information is often not even considered with ongoing processes or with political initiatives. Existing inappropriate information systems may continue to be used, providing the wrong incentives or making new priorities or targets more difficult to achieve.

Nature of information and styles of use

There are many aspects of healthcare where hard information – facts and figures – is just not available to inform a decision. Softer information must be used, such as views, opinions, thoughts and feelings. However, in general there is more good hard information available than is ever used. Published information, knowledge-based and policy information is easily and quickly available via the Internet as well as from longer-established sources. Statistical information abounds.[6] Policy information is readily available from Government departments and professional bodies. What is lacking is a desire to seek out information, a knowledge of what is available where, and an expectation that others will demand evidence.

Views and opinions are brought together with hard information in business cases, discussion documents and consultation papers (*see* Figure 1.4).

Figure 1.4 Hard and soft information.

For the outline of a business case, *see* Appendix 1.

In all cases it should be possible to put forward a logical rational argument, whether it is based on hard or soft information, and in all cases those making the argument will be selective about the information that they present. It is human nature to expect people to put emphasis on that information which supports their case, while playing down that which does not support the case. There is often a view that it is for others to present the contra-argument.

Different people tend to use information in different ways. The Myers–Briggs Type Indicator (MBTI)[7] describes the preferences that everyone has with regard to how they use information to make decisions (*see* Table 1.1). At one extreme there are people who have a preference for only using tangible information that they can put into a planned logical format (intuitives/thinkers/judges). A large proportion of technicians fall into this category. At the other extreme there are those who prefer to use 'soft' information – things they are told, see and feel – based on whether it reinforces their values. A large proportion of nurses fall into this category. These two extreme uses of information illustrate one of the main reasons for poor communication between different groups in both allocation and management of resources.

Table 1.1 MBTI types

Preference	MBTI subscale		
Focusing on the world	Extroverts	. . . .	Introverts
Acquiring information	Intuitives	. . . .	Sensors
Making decisions	Thinkers	. . . .	Feelers
Approaching life	Judges	. . . .	Perceivers

This often leads to much misunderstanding, where the different types of information use are not appreciated and different types of people are trying to reach to a decision together.

It is often assumed that lack of training in the appropriate information to use, what is available, how to use it and what it means is at the heart of failure to use information. Although training is essential, and many healthcare staff would benefit from training in all aspects of information use, training is not the whole story. When faced with a decision, *intuitive/thinker/judges* are probably thinking: 'If only I give them the figures and explain them, they will understand'. *Sensor/feeler/perceivers* could well be thinking 'Lies, damned lies and statistics – who needs them? Just ask an expert'.

Words and figures can both be used to clarify and explain, and also to hide and deceive. Some people prefer words and some prefer figures, but the powerful use both of them.

People can be viewed on a scale ranging from information averse to information seeking (*see* Figure 1.5). Unless it is integrated into management processes, there is no imperative to use management

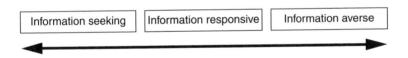

Figure 1.5 Information culture.

information. Those who are information seeking by nature will find the relevant information and use it to support decision making, whereas those who are information averse will not.

Senior managers have an important role in influencing behaviour. If they themselves are information seeking, then they are more likely to encourage this from others. If not, they will tend to reward other behaviours.

The changing way in which management information is being presented has both positive and negative influences on the use of that information. Increasingly, information is being placed on the Internet and local intranets. This makes a much wider range and far greater volume of information readily accessible. It also means that, rather than information appearing in a manager's in-tray, managers must now seek out that information. While this favours those who are information seeking, it means that those who are information averse will tend to manage with less information than before.

There are three essential aspects to encouraging greater use:

- integration into management processes
- senior managers as role models for seeking and using information
- training and development in the changing availability and use of information.

Information: a driver for change

Information is often considered to be a major driver for change, as indeed it is, but merely making information available will not in itself drive change. There are other ingredients, including political will, supply and demand pressures, technological developments and many more. For years the NHS has had more data than it knows what to do with. Practical examples of how it can be used abound. Given the will and the skills, it has been possible to use this information in management processes, but the pressures have not been there to ensure that this happens. It does not need more data. However, lack of data and lack of information have often been used as excuses for avoiding change.

It is true that there are technical issues to be resolved, such as the accuracy and timeliness of information, but there are other issues as well, including the following:

- lack of demand from senior, commissioning or regulatory bodies
- lack of knowledge of what is available or how it can be used
- limited or slow access to data or tools for analysis and presentation
- lack of technical and statistical know-how in information analysis.

It is behaviours, not structures, that drive organisations. If information is to be effective as a driver for change, it needs to influence the following:

- beliefs and values
- motivation and commitment
- rewards and incentives
- power
- loyalties
- personal hopes and fears
- informal communication
- routines.

Changing behaviour

Use of information as an integral part of management processes is a powerful way in which to change the decision-making behaviour of individuals.

> **Example 1.2** Clinical care
>
> A consultant was reviewing the postoperative infection rate of his patients who underwent a specific procedure. He knew that some of his patients had infections, and that this had resulted in them having to stay in hospital for longer. He did not realise the extent of the problem until he saw all of the patients undergoing this particular procedure listed together, and his infection rates for this procedure compared with those of his colleagues elsewhere. After this he did things differently, with better results.

Example 1.3 Waiting-lists

Maximum waiting-times and size of waiting-list are two common performance measures for hospital surgical specialities. There are incentives for an organisation to meet the targets and put pressure on individuals to deliver.

- *Actions to reduce waiting-list size* include discouraging entry on to the list, ensuring that everyone on the list really is waiting, and undertaking many quick simple procedures rather than a few complex procedures.
- *Actions to reduce maximum waiting-time* are different, and include admitting those patients who are reaching the maximum time, and delaying entry on to the list.

Few people would argue that either of these strategies puts clinical need for treatment at the top of the decision tree. This is not to say that monitoring waiting-lists using either or both of these measures is not an essential thing to do – indeed it is. The behaviour that is generated when incentives are provided to influence either inputs or part of the process (as in this example) does not necessarily generate the desired outputs or outcomes.

Changing process

Most of the operational work of healthcare organisations is subject to well-defined and documented processes. For example, the diagnostic process in clinical practice is the subject of much research and publication. Administration processes, such as admitting a patient or making an appointment, are similarly documented. Consider some of the following examples:

- ordering a diagnostic test and receiving the results (order communications)
- monitoring expenditure against budget (management budgeting)
- paying the workforce (payroll processing).

These processes will almost certainly be accompanied at various stages by filling in a form electronically or on paper and sending it to another person or department, where further stages of the process are carried out, based on the information that is given. Defined processes have many advantages, including avoiding confusion where several people are involved in the process, ensuring that details are not missed, and avoiding errors.

However, there are disadvantages of those well-defined processes. Changes in the environment over time mean that the process may not remain the most effective or efficient way to achieve an outcome. In particular, changes in the availability of information or the way in which it can be communicated often make changes desirable. An individual who is involved in part of a process will rightly be reluctant to make any incremental change in case it has an adverse effect elsewhere, but will often add extra bits to the process.

Review of process and making information readily available directly linked to process change is a powerful way of optimising well-defined processes. Moreover, because once learned these processes are followed, it is a powerful way both of ensuring a defined quality standard and of influencing behaviour. Failure to redesign processes leads to the following:

- duplication of process – those involved take on new processes but fail to drop redundant processes, mainly because they don't know whether or not stopping some activities will have an adverse effect on others
- duplication of information – people continue to collect the information used on both the new and redundant processes
- lack of commitment to or confidence in new processes, and less than enthusiastic participation in them.

Effective and efficient use of information

The definition of information requirements, its production and interpretation all take time and are costly. As with any other investment, it is necessary to consider whether that investment in information is worthwhile. There are means by which the efficiency and effectiveness of gathering and using information can be improved. In particular, when defining information requirements it is important to identify which of the following is most appropriate:

- retrospective or prospective information
- continuous monitoring or ad hoc exercises
- use of exception reporting.

Retrospective vs. prospective information

Retrospective information allows us to find out what has gone wrong and to change it. However, there can be a considerable time lag between the action and its identification.

Prospective information ensures that we get it right first time and avoid things going wrong.

Both types of information are essential for effective and efficient use of resources. Prospective information allows us to get it right first time, but retrospective information allows us to monitor for those cases where we don't.

Example 1.4 Clinical governance

A major aspect of clinical governance is ensuring the effective and efficient provision and use of resources to optimise clinical outcome. Many attempts at providing information to support clinical governance are based on the retrospective collection and analysis of information 'to seek out the bad apple'. Although this is essential, it often takes many months or even years before poor practice can be demonstrated, as the numbers of similar cases that can provide direct comparisons are often too small to demonstrate statistical significance. A proactive approach linking information directly to clinical processes can mean that failures are identified and acted upon before they adversely affect individual patient care. For example, ensuring that the right drug is delivered in the right dose to the right site on the right patient can be embedded into a routine process. Information support for effective clinical processes, such as automatic alerts, cross-referencing clinical data and prompting actions based on protocols, helps to prevent failure from occurring. Taking a 'black-box' approach (monitoring inputs and outputs from a process) using speciality-specific measures is most likely to produce gains. For example, hospitals that have implemented order communications or electronic patient record systems now receive an alert if the medication they are about to prescribe has contraindications, or conflicts with other medications that the patient is receiving.

Example 1.5 Management budgeting

Most NHS management budgeting processes involve the issuing of monthly reports showing all payments that have been made by the organisation against individual budgets. There is a delay between a financial commitment being made (e.g. placing an order) and the payment of an invoice. A delay of up to nine months for quite substantial commitments is not unusual. This often means that a budget holder is not entirely sure of their financial position at any point in the year, and of whether they are going to end the year under or over budget, unless they keep a note of these commitments. It would help everyone if the prospective as well as the retrospective processes ran alongside each other. Keeping a note of sums committed against a budget when an order is placed, and not just after the order has been fulfilled and payment has been made, can add to a manager's ability to control a budget.

Continuous monitoring vs. ad hoc exercises

With the increasing use of operational electronic systems to support patient care (electronic patient records) and the continuing fall in the cost of information technology, it is now relatively easy and cheap to monitor resource use continuously across an organisation. The cost of ad hoc exercises is principally due to the skilled people required to define and produce the information, and it is a relatively expensive option.

It is possible to monitor continuously variations in actual practice from that which is expected across a wide range of variables. These include the following:

- activity, utilisation and cost
- inputs, process events and outcome
- defined performance indicators
- for the organisation compared with other organisations
- for individual consultants, specialties and departments
- adjusted for case mix and population variables
- monitored against targets, standards, expectations and protocols.

This creates a great deal of information that needs to be interpreted and acted upon. Extensive routine monitoring needs to be linked with automatic alerting when values exceed predetermined levels (*see* 'Exception reporting' below). Most organisations currently employ two strategies:

- monitoring only those performance indicators that are demanded by external organisations
- adding to this internal performance indicators either as refinements of those demanded by external organisations or in areas of concern.

There is a valid concern with regard to extending routine monitoring. The information highlights variation but cannot suggest whether that variation is warranted, has arisen by chance or raises a matter that needs to be dealt with. This can only be determined by further investigation. The cost will outweigh the benefit where too often the information is defined in such a way as to highlight matters that turn out not to be of concern. Careful initial investigation and design using standardised variables wherever possible reduces this possibility.

Exception reporting

Exception reporting is the name given to the process whereby a great deal of information is routinely monitored electronically but only reported if the values exceed a predefined value.

The aim is to avoid spending a great deal of time searching through tables and reports, either on paper or on screen, only to find that most of it is indicating that everything is fine and on track and no action is required.

Exception reporting has applications in all aspects of management of resources.

The predefined values will come from a variety of sources, including the following:

- objectives that have been set to be achieved within a certain period – intermediate milestones can be set to monitor progress towards the objective

- best practice guidelines, targets or standards

- the norm or expectation – setting the average achievement of other groups or organisations as an initial target.

Key points

- Healthcare operates within a complex environment with many influential stakeholders with different goals.
- Changes in the external environment add to the complexity.
- A balance needs to be struck between the use of hard and soft information, and between the rational–logical argument and the political–social argument.
- Different people perceive and use information in different ways.
- The effectiveness of information use can be greatly enhanced by integrating information into management processes.
- Information can be an effective driver for change by altering both behaviour and process.
- The effectiveness and efficiency of information use can be enhanced by a variety of techniques.

References

1   Department of Health (2000) *An Organisation with a Memory*. Department of Health, London.

2   Bullas S (2000) Evidence-based management. In: W Abbott, J Bryant and S Bullas (eds) *Current Perspectives in Health Informatics*. British Computer Society, Swindon.

3   Rigby M (1999) *Realising the Fundamental Role of Information in Health Care Delivery and Management: reducing the zone of confusion*. Nuffield Trust, London.

4   Roberts R (1999) *Information for Evidence-Based Care*. Harnessing Health Information Series. Radcliffe Medical Press, Oxford.

5   Northcott J (1991) *Britain in 2010: the PSI Report*. PSI Publishing, London.

6   Leadbetter D (2000) *Harnessing Official Statistics*. Harnessing Health Information Series. Radcliffe Medical Press, Oxford.

7   Beins B, Feldman AJ and Gall SB (eds) (1996) Myers-Briggs Type Indicator. In: *Gale Encyclopaedia of Psychology*. Gale Group.

2　The workforce

Introduction

Healthcare is a service provided by people, in purpose-built premises or anywhere else, using equipment and consumables to address a healthcare need and produce a desired outcome. Nearly one million people are directly employed by the NHS hospital and community health services, equivalent to around 780 000 whole-time equivalents. The workforce is the most important resource in providing quality outcomes. It is also the most expensive resource, accounting for around 65% of the revenue expenditure of health authorities and NHS trusts.[1]

The workforce really is the most valued and valuable resource, but how often are these words backed up by action?

Health organisations compete for staff within an overall labour market where those seeking work have many choices for employment. In order to attract recruits, these organisations must offer a working environment and conditions that make them an employer of choice. To do this, they need to know what existing staff and potential recruits think about the working environment and how the working environment compares with that of other major employers.

It is essential that a motivated workforce with appropriate skills and experience is employed in all parts of healthcare. It is also essential that different disciplines work together in multidisciplinary teams, and that the structures and processes are in place to ensure that they are able to do a good job.

It is also critical that all members of a team have the confidence to express any concerns they may have about the working of the team and its interaction with other parts of the organisation, without fear of being disadvantaged by doing so. An organisation that 'shoots the messenger' is not one that can learn and improve. A recent survey[2] of over 20 000 staff in a variety of healthcare organisations found that less than one-third felt that staff were confident about expressing their views and concerns.

Information about the workforce and their views is essential if a high-quality service is to be provided. In addition, information about the local community, labour market and alternative employers is essential in order to maintain a skilled workforce when external pressures and demand for service change.

Much of that information is readily available from existing personnel and payroll systems, but is not exploited to its full potential. For example, simple profiles of the workforce (e.g. by age, gender, department, profession or residence) provide valuable information about retirement patterns and needs for future recruitment. Turnover and sickness levels provide valuable indicators of the working environment and the morale of staff.

Structure of the workforce

Of the nearly one million people who were employed in the NHS hospital and community health services in 1999, 68% were direct care staff and 32% were management and support staff. The figures presented in this section are taken from the Department of Health, Health and Personal Social Services Statistics for England.[1]

Table 2.1 provides further details.

Table 2.1 Staffing statistics

Staffing category	Whole-time equivalents (thousands) in 1999
All directly employed staff	782.1
All direct care staff	529.3
Nurses, midwives and health-visiting staff	338.6
Medical and dental staff	60.3
Other	130.4
All management and support staff	252.8
Administration and estates staff	172.8
Other management and support staff	80.0

In addition, Table 2.2 shows the numbers of general medical practitioners and practice staff.

Table 2.2 General practitioners and practice staff

Staffing category	Whole-time equivalents (thousands) in 1999
Practitioners (unrestricted practitioners and equivalent)	25.9
Practice staff	
Practice nurses	10.7
Direct patient care	1.9
Administration and clerical	50.0
Other	0.5

The workforce is our most valued and valuable resource

Most NHS organisations would agree that their workforce is their most valuable resource. Most would also subscribe to the view that the workforce is valued. But how many actually demonstrate this through the environment that is provided, the remuneration and the services that are available to staff? Too often it is a phrase in the annual report and not one that is experienced by the workforce.

Providing a suitably trained workforce with the required numbers of staff is one of today's major challenges. It has a direct impact on the quantity and quality of care and treatment offered, and it also has an impact on the bottom line – ineffective recruitment, high turnover rates and high levels of sickness/absenteeism all contribute to waste and cost.

In small organisations (e.g. a GP practice) it is easy to know what the workforce thinks, as there will be personal contact on a daily basis. In large organisations, and many healthcare providers are very large organisations indeed, it is more difficult. Ask them (*see* page 33 on 'What does the workforce think?').

Recent work has shown that bullying and harassment are widespread.[2] In the *Positively Diverse* study, staff were asked whether they had experienced harassment and bullying during the previous 12 months. At that time almost a third of ethnic minority staff said that they had experienced harassment and bullying due to their racial background. One in seven of both male and female staff experienced harassment and bullying due to their gender. A similar level of harassment was experienced by staff on the grounds of disability. There was some reported harassment of white staff on the grounds of race, and of all staff on the grounds of age.

Turnover rates and levels of sickness and absenteeism are also useful indicators of whether staff feel that they are valued.

Recent policy statements and initiatives have put an emphasis on ensuring an appropriate workforce. The NHS Executive strategy *Working Together*[3] set the following three workforce aims:

- to ensure that we have a quality workforce, in the right numbers, with the right skills and diversity and organised in the right way to deliver the Government's service objectives for health and social care
- to be able to demonstrate that we are improving the quality of working life for staff
- to address the management capacity and capability required to deliver this agenda and the associated programme of change.

How do we know what is 'right'? How do we know whether things are improving or whether we have the capacity and capability? We need to set targets, measure baselines and monitor progress.

The NHS Plan[4] set workforce targets for more staff, more training places, new medical school places, improved pay and improved working lives. *Improving Working Lives (IWL)* sets out a standard that all NHS organisations must meet by April 2003. This standard[5] specifies a great deal of evidence that accreditation teams will expect to find within each organisation. Providing the necessary evidence will involve most organisations in significant development of their information systems. Meeting the first stage alone involves providing evidence of the following:

1 human resource strategy to support service targets
2 meeting human resource performance targets
3 board commitment to:
   - team-based employee self-rostering
   - annual-hours arrangements
   - childcare support
   - reduced-hours options
   - flexitime
   - carers support
   - career breaks
   - flexible retirement
4 building a diverse workforce that reflects the local community

5 changing the long-hours culture
6 healthy workplace environment
7 managers leading by example
8 finding out what working arrangements work for staff
9 challenging traditional working patterns
10 involving staff in the design and development of better, flexible working practices
11 conducting annual staff-attitude surveys – asking relevant questions and acting on key messages
12 human resource policies and processes that make a difference to individuals
13 accessible training and development packages for all staff.

Competing for staff

Healthcare organisations are competing for staff with other employers both within the local area and further afield. There are a number of factors that determine how successful organisations are in attracting staff. Figure 2.1 summarises the competitive forces.

Figure 2.1 Competing for staff.

An assessment of the factors shown in Figure 2.1 can focus action where it is likely to be most effective.

Demographics

The size and age structure of the population served is the largest factor in determining demand for health services. However, this factor is changing. The following forecasts were made for changes in the population of the UK between 1990 and 2010:[6]

- probably a total increase of 2.6 million (4.6%)
- a faster increase than in the period 1970–90
- no further fall in the number of teenagers
- a fall of 2.4 million in the number of young adults
- higher average age of the working population
- little change in the total number aged 65 to 79 years
- an increase of 600 000 in those over 80 years of age.

In many parts of the country there are planned population changes (e.g. house-building programmes responding to differential employment opportunities). Local, small-area population figures and forecasts are available from the census that is taken every 10 years and from local authority planning departments. The latest census in the UK was conducted in April 2001, although the results only start to become available a considerable time after that. The size and age structure of the population impacts not only on the demand for health services, but also the on supply of staff. There are different changes in different parts of the country, with those of younger working age drawn to particular geographical areas, leaving a higher proportion of older people needing more healthcare. The structure of the workforce itself is important. For example the age structure and projected retirement patterns may indicate impending difficulties. The Policy Studies Institute Report forecast a decline in the potential labour force of about one million (3.5%) due to an increase in the numbers in full-time education and training.[6]

A rich source of population information is available from National Statistics.[7] Their website allows you to search the latest and most comprehensive official statistics and information in the UK, including the most recently available census data. Local population figures are readily available from local authorities, and in many cases they will be published on the Internet.

Local employment

Understanding the local employment profile is essential for successful recruitment. Healthcare organisations are in competition with other local employers for a skilled workforce, both for entrants into training and for more experienced staff.

The following questions need to be asked about the working population.

- What is the size and age profile of the working population?
- What is the skill level of the working population?
- What is the level of unemployment?
- What is the ethnic structure of the organisation?

The following questions need to be asked about the employers.

- Who are the major employers?
- Are they employing people with the same skills and experience as the healthcare organisation?

This information will be readily available from the local authority, as Example 2.1 demonstrates.

Example 2.1 An investigation of the Cambridgeshire County Council Labour Force Survey information

This investigation found the following information about the local community.
  Between 1994 and 1998:
- the overall number of resident working males remained largely unchanged
- the female resident workforce increased by about 1%
- there was an increase in the potential resident labour force (population $\geqslant 16$ years of age)
- the overall economic activity rate has declined slightly.
In 1998:
- unemployment as defined by the International Labour Organisation was about 5%.
Employment by industry sector is shown in the following table.

Industry sector	Mean 1996–98 (%)	Change
Public, education, health	23.9%	Stable
Manufacturing	20.0%	Decline
Distribution and catering	19.6%	Stable
Business services, R&D	15.2%	Growth
Other services	6.1%	
Transport and communications	6.0%	
Construction	5.4%	
Agriculture	2.7%	
Energy	0.8%	
Not known	0.3%	

Earnings in Cambridgeshire were broadly similar to the national average. Mean weekly earnings were £405. Nearly 22% of all employees earned under £250 per week. This is less than for the UK as a whole.

The decline in manufacturing might make it easier to recruit staff with certain skills. The growth in business services and R&D is likely to make it more difficult to recruit staff in these areas. It may be necessary to expend additional effort or consider carefully working conditions in the areas of business services and R&D in order to retain or recruit staff in these areas.

Sources:
http://www.nationalstatistics.gov.uk
http://www.camcnty.gov.uk

Is the healthcare organisation competitive in terms of:

- the terms and conditions of employment, particularly in areas of flexible working?
- the salaries offered?

Cost of living

Another factor that needs to be taken into account is the local cost of living. A high cost of living may deter potential employees from moving into the area. Those who are already living in the area or moving into it may seek a higher financial reward than the healthcare organisation can provide. Salary enhancements based on the relative cost of living of an area can help to alleviate the situation.

Cost-of-living information is available from a variety of sources, including local authorities, the Institute for Fiscal Studies,[8] and the Reward Group.[9]

> **Example 2.2** Housing costs
>
> High housing costs are forcing almost all nurses and other key workers to contemplate leaving London or their jobs, according to a survey by the Greater London Authority. The study found that nurses want to live closer to work and are more likely than those in other occupations, such as police and teachers, to want to move home.
>
> News in Brief, *Health Services Journal*, 15 February 2001.

Diversity

There are very good economic as well as moral reasons for managing diversity in the workforce.

- Drawing from all sections of the community increases the likelihood of being able to recruit the staff that are needed.
- A diverse workforce is better positioned to develop a cultural competency in understanding the diverse needs of those it serves, particularly the cultural and religious needs of minority groups. It is important that healthcare services respect the needs of different groups with regard to matters of birth, death, privacy, personal care, meals, ritual and ceremony.

The *Positively Diverse* study,[2,10] which covers more than 20 000 staff in over 30 healthcare and social care organisations, quantified the diversity of the workforce compared with that in the community. The information content includes the following:

- diversity of the local community
- diversity of the workforce
- views of the workforce.

Two important performance measures that indicate whether an organisation is diverse are:

- whether the profile of the workforce matches the profile of the local community of working age, with regard to age, gender and ethnic origin
- the extent to which this is reflected throughout the organisation – in professional and senior management posts as well as more junior roles.

These measures should not be aims in their own right, but rather give a reflection of the state of the organisation. It is the underlying issues such as fairness to all staff, developing talent and opening up employment opportunities to all sections of the community which will ensure that performance is improved.

Changing profiles in professional groups involves training schools and universities recruiting from all sections of the community. Recruitment of trained and qualified professional staff can only be from the appropriately trained and qualified subset of the population. It would therefore take some years to influence any imbalance at senior levels of the professions.

In time, an organisation that manages diversity should see the following:

- an increase in the number of individuals from minority ethnic groups entering professional training, which will increase the confidence of all sectors of the community with regard to using services
- lower turnover of staff from minority ethnic groups, and less early retirement due to disability, which will reduce recruitment and retraining costs
- reduced levels of sickness and absence due to stress and violent incidents, which will lead to reduced costs for relief staff
- reduced risk of Industrial Tribunals or other legal challenges, with all of the costs, adverse publicity and strains on management time that these would entail
- a more confident workforce which is more willing to embrace change
- better patient care from an increasingly culturally competent workforce which is more understanding and informed about cultural, economic and social aspects of disease.

These objectives suggest other measures that are important for monitoring the workforce. Examples 2.3 and 2.4 demonstrate a simple information set by which an acute hospital trust and a mental health trust monitor ethnic diversity within the workforce.

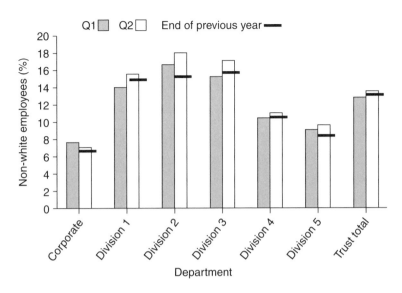

Figure 2.2 Workforce ethnic minority profile.

Example 2.3 Meeting organisational objectives for diversity and equality

This analysis is routinely undertaken by an acute hospital trust in order to monitor the ethnic profile of the workforce. The organisational objectives for diversity and equality are agreed on the basis of a strategic analysis of the current situation.

Organisational objective: Ensure that there is a committed and motivated workforce.
Sub-objective 1: Implement equal opportunities, communication, staff well-being and involvement strategies to create a more responsive, safer and better engaged organisation.
Sub-objective 2: Develop a users' forum to improve communication and identify and implement two measurable service improvements within each division.

Milestones
After 1 year:
- a schedule identifying national, regional and trust targets has been developed
- consultative committees are established in all divisions
- an internal communications plan has been agreed by the trust board
- a trust-wide framework for staff well-being and equal opportunities has been established
- the trust is corporately working towards national targets.

Monitoring information
Figure 2.2 shows the information that is used to monitor the percentage of non-white employees in the different parts of the organisation over time. It shows the position six months into the year.

Example 2.4 Comparing the ethnic profile of the workforce with the community profile

This analysis was undertaken by a mental health NHS trust.

The aim of the exercise was to determine whether the workforce reflected the community and whether the responders to a workforce survey reflected the make-up of the entire workforce.

Ethnicity	Respondents (%)	Workforce (%)	Community (%)
White	76.5	68.7	85.3
Black	10.5	17.3	3.3
Indian	3.0	8.0	7.9
Pakistani	0.0	0.0	1.9
Bangladeshi	0.5	0.3	0.8
Other/not known	5.5	5.3	0.8

It is often assumed that black and ethnic minorities are under-represented within the workforce because of failure to attract from all sectors in the community. This was not so in the case of this trust, where black staff form a much higher proportion of the workforce than in the local community. On further investigation, the trust found that this balance was not reflected throughout the organisation, and that there were few black and ethnic minority staff in senior management positions.

Focus for change was placed on training assessment, promotion opportunities and management recruitment and development to ensure that it was fair to all.

Sources:

Results of *Positively Diverse* audit

Personnel database

1991 Census

A workforce 'fit for purpose': recruitment, working environment and training

Recruitment

Expenditure on recruitment is considerable, and includes the cost of advertising, administration, and time spent by the panel shortlisting and interviewing. Much of this is wasted – not because the process itself is inefficient, but because much of the activity would be avoided if unnecessary turnover were to be eliminated.

Turnover of staff, leading to the need for recruitment, can be positive when development leads to promotions. There will be a natural level of turnover due to retirement, personal circumstances and other factors. However, some turnover (e.g. where it stems from dissatisfaction with the working environment or unacceptable working hours) is often unnecessary and results in poor quality, and wasted costs of recruitment, induction and training of others. Turnover levels are normally well known, but unnecessary turnover is only identified from exit interviews.

Ineffective advertising, or advertising that is not reaching sectors of the community where potential recruits might be found, results in abortive recruitment effort. It is of little use to focus on recruitment if recruits find that the actual working environment is not as fair as they were led to believe. Any dissatisfaction will soon be communicated throughout the community, resulting in a lower response to future recruitment campaigns.

These examples are given to demonstrate that much of the human resource information is linked and needs to be interpreted as a whole. There is little point in having effective recruitment if new recruits find a poorer working environment than they had been led to believe existed. Moreover, there is little point in spending resources on recruitment when job offers and the working environment are not attractive or competitive.

For effective recruitment, the following questions need to be considered.

1   What response does the organisation get from advertising campaigns?
2   How much does it cost to fill a vacancy?
3   How does this compare with similar organisations?
4   Does the profile of the workforce mirror that of the community?
5   How is the organisation perceived as an employer by the local community?
6   What other organisations are competing for the same staff?
    - school leavers
    - general skill jobs
    - healthcare professionals.

Working environment

The working environment of healthcare staff is characterised by considerable pressure.

One factor that is important for ensuring a stable workforce, reducing turnover, improving recruitment and reducing levels of sickness/absenteeism, is to improve the opportunities for all staff to achieve their desired balance between work time and home time. Flexible working is a major contributor to this.

Organisations are beginning to gather evidence that an improved working environment has an economic as well as a moral argument in its favour. A business case can now be made for investments in this area.

Four healthcare organisations (see below) feature in the Department for Education and Employment (DfEE) Work Life Balance Case Studies.[11]

Oxford Radcliffe Hospital is well aware of the cost of recruitment and the impact that this has on the overall costs of the trust (*see* Example 2.5). This information is readily available, but how many other healthcare organisations use it?

Example 2.5 Oxford Radcliffe Hospital NHS Trust

Oxford Radcliffe Hospital NHS Trust opened the Roosevelt Centre on 1 September 1999 as the first elder day-care facility aimed at their employees. The trust has 7400 staff and needs to retain and attract the highest-quality staff (the cost of recruitment is currently around £5000 per member of staff). The Centre provides a safe and stimulating environment for people who are dependent on their family for care.

It is not just large organisations that can benefit, as is shown by Example 2.6.

Example 2.6 Cheshire Health Agency

Cheshire Health Agency (small employer category winner of the Parents at Work Award 1999) employs 110 people. The agency recognises the demands of home life and work responsibilities, and has a range of policies in place, including paid paternity leave, paid and unpaid adoption leave, and paid carer leave. Staff are involved in deciding on cover. So long as the work is done and deadlines are met, they can work hours to suit themselves within a flexitime system. The benefits are that trained and skilled staff are retained, and savings are made on recruitment and training.

When Newham Community Trust assessed the results of introducing flexible working practices, they found that these avoided considerable recruitment effort (*see* Example 2.7).

Example 2.7 Newham Community Trust

Newham Community Trust is one NHS organisation that is already beginning to reap the benefits of *flexible working practices*. The trust identified the fact that many staff were leaving because of the difficulty of balancing work and home responsibilities. After consultation with staff and the joint staff committee, a number of work initiatives were introduced, including home working, job sharing and annualised hours. The latest figures show that of the 60 staff who are taking advantage of the new policy, over half would have been forced to leave had these flexible arrangements not been available.

North Manchester General Hospital found that similar measures helped them to cope with the variable demand throughout the year (*see* Example 2.8).

> **Example 2.8** North Manchester General Hospital
>
> Nurses in the Medical Directorate at North Manchester General Hospital have developed an annualised-hours scheme to complement other equal opportunities and family-friendly policies designed to attract and retain staff in a hard-to-recruit inner-city hospital. The Medical Directorate has 97% bed occupancy, high patient turnover rates, and is acknowledged as an area where nurses are working under pressure. The objective is to equalise supply and demand for staff through the seasonal peaks and troughs in activity, and to enable staff to work in new patterns which suit them better. A more efficient use of staff time has been achieved, corresponding to seasonal fluctuations in demand for care. Staff have tended to consolidate owed time in blocks, especially during the summer holidays, when activity rates are at their lowest. Staff say that the scheme has given them greater control over their own lives. They have become more motivated, and patient care has benefited as a result.

In order to achieve a balance, there is a need to challenge assumptions – most healthcare organisations can provide more flexibility than they initially imagine. A study undertaken by the NHS Executive looked at the benefits of family-friendly working practices (regardless of the composition of the family, e.g. parents with young children or single people), the contribution that self-rostering made to achieving this, and the information support required. More importantly, it looked at the management issues involved and the integration of information into management processes. The results of this study were documented in a report with the misleading title *Self-Rostering Software* – in fact, the least significant aspect of the study was the software used to support the processes.[12]

Flexible working is becoming more common, but it does have greater information needs than working practices where all staff are working similar hours week in, week out. Some organisations have been imaginative in the flexibility that they have found they can offer, including the following:

- annualised hours
- term-time contracts
- holiday-time contracts
- hours to fit in with child-care arrangements and social commitments
- carer leave and paternity leave
- home working

- hours to fit in with travelling arrangements
- long shifts over three days.

A balanced workforce is achieved when the needs of the organisation for skills, experience and time are balanced with the needs of individual staff. This requires an understanding by the organisation both of its own needs and its staff needs, assessed through workforce planning, staff appraisal and staff-attitude studies.

There is a need to be fair to all staff, regardless of whether they are single, parents with young children, have dependants, are disabled or have varying cultural backgrounds. On occasion this will require positive action to establish fairness for a specific group. The first step is knowledge and understanding.

For effective flexible working there is a need to know the following:

- the organisation's needs for skills, hours and other criteria throughout the day/week
- the needs of the individuals available to work those hours, based on whatever criteria those individuals choose
- a way of matching the two sets of needs.

Training

For clinical staff and other professions where there is a statutory requirement for specific qualifications and registration, the information to ensure that the training matches the statutory requirements is routinely held on operational personnel information systems. Registration of clinical professions ensures that standards are assessed and, increasingly, that skills and knowledge are kept up to date. This State Registration is increasingly being extended to cover further professions. For example, from October 2000 it is a statutory requirement for all clinical scientists in the UK to register with the Clinical Science Board of the Council for Professions Supplementary to Medicine, and from June 2001 it is a criminal offence for anyone to describe themselves as a chiropractor if they are not registered with the General Chiropractic Council.

However, for other staff, including informatics staff and managers, the assessment, provision and recording of training are less rigorous. In some places, formal procedures are in place but in many there is insufficient information available.

The initial questions to be asked are as follows.

- How are training and development needs assessed?
- Do all employees have a fair opportunity for their development?
- What training opportunities are available and are these appropriate to meet the training needs of the workforce?

The following question then arises.

- How are these training needs to be met?

Readily accessible information on in-house training courses, courses at academic institutions and external trainers and coaches is necessary.

It is then important to have a record of who has received what training.

Experience and on-the-job training are just as important as formal training and qualifications for many positions. Any recording and use of training information should not be allowed to overshadow this.

What does the workforce think?

If appropriate measures are to be taken to improve the working lives of staff, it is essential to find out their views on the working environment and their expectations of it. One of the targets of the Human Resources Performance Framework is that all NHS employers should conduct an annual staff-attitude survey.

A general attitude survey may cover many aspects of the working environment, such as the following:

- working hours
- pay and conditions
- flexibility
- understanding of policies and procedures
- extent to which home and work life can be balanced
- training and development opportunities
- relationships
- appraisal methods
- experience and sources of harassment and bullying
- confidence about expressing concerns
- physical working environment

- level of appreciation felt
- support from within the organisation.

Exit interviews (interviewing staff who are leaving) may be considered to be shutting the stable door after the horse has bolted. However, such interviews are essential if the organisation is to know how much of staff turnover is positive or unavoidable (e.g. career progression, change in personal circumstances, etc.) and how much is avoidable (e.g. pressure and stress, harassment and bullying, inability to balance work and home life, etc.).

When designing surveys, the following general points should be considered.

- Try to avoid making the questionnaire too long. Potential respondents might be put off completing it at all if they feel that it would be too time-consuming.
- Avoid adding questions which, while you might be interested in obtaining responses to them, are not directly related to the overall objective of the audit (e.g., a question about whether staff like the new format of the staff newsletter).
- Avoid making individual questions, and the questionnaire as a whole, appear complicated to answer. Keep the questions as simple and explicit as possible.
- When composing a question, consider how you might want to analyse it when you have the responses. This might influence how the question is constructed (e.g. yes/no/don't know, multiple choice, or free text).
- If you want to compare responses from different organisations, the questionnaires will need to be the same or very similar.

Confidentiality of responses is important. Staff are more likely to give an honest response if they know that they cannot be identified, especially in an organisation where there is a low level of confidence about expressing concerns. There are ways in which an individual can be identified other than by name. For example, there is often a desire to find out the views of individual departments or professional groups. Where individual characteristics have been asked for, such as age, sex and ethnic group, these together with the work group or department might mean that an individual is identified.

Impact on improving clinical care: expressing concerns

The overwhelming majority of healthcare staff want to provide the best possible care for patients and clients, with the best possible outcomes. However, unless everyone has the confidence to express their concerns and to have these taken seriously, this will not happen.

Increasingly it is being recognised that many failures of clinical care are due to the overall system and not to any one individual within it. However, often it is an individual who pays the penalty. An important way of identifying potential points of failure and improving the system to ensure that these are avoided is to allow full and frank discussion among all of those involved.

The *Positively Diverse* audit identified a low level of confidence about expressing concerns within those organisations that took part in the audit. Why should they be unwilling to express their concerns?

- It will adversely affect their careers to do so.
- The organisation 'shoots the messenger'.
- They will be harassed as a result, and branded as a trouble maker.

It will take more than the NHS Executive saying that such behaviour is unacceptable, and it will take more than the organisation having a whistle-blowing policy, to overcome such lack of confidence about expressing concerns.

Key points

- The workforce is the most *valuable* resource and should be the most *valued* resource.
- A high-quality service can only be provided in a good working environment where all staff are treated fairly and they can express concerns without disadvantage – know what the workforce think.
- Healthcare organisations compete for staff with other employers – know the local employment situation and whether the organisation is competitive within it.
- Diversity is not only a moral issue: there are economic arguments as well.
- What does the workforce think? Ask them. How do the responses compare with those from other organisations?

References

1   http:/www.doh.gov.uk/HPSSS/INDEX.HTM
2   NHS Executive (2000) *Positively Diverse Report 2000.* NHS Executive, Leeds.
3   Department of Health (1998) *Working Together.* Department of Health, London.
4   Department of Health (2000) *NHS Plan: a plan for investment, a plan for reform.* Department of Health, London.
5   Department of Health (2000) *Improving Working Lives Standard.* Department of Health, London.
6   Northcott J (1991) *Britain in 2010: the PSI Report.* PSI Publishing, London.
7   http://www.statistics.gov.uk/
8   Institute for Fiscal Studies; www.ifs.org.uk
9   Reward Group; www.reward-group.co.uk
10 Department of Health (2001) *Positively Diverse: field book.* Department of Health, London.
11 www.dfee.gov.uk/work-lifebalance/case.htm
12 NHS Executive (1988) *Self Rostering Software: time care pilot evaluation. Final report.* NHS Executive, Leeds.

3 Managing the estate and supplies

Introduction

If staff are the most important resource in the NHS, then the next most important resource consists of the facilities and environment within which they provide care, and the supplies and materials that they have at their disposal. Without effective financial and quality management of the estate, support facilities and supplies, a trust's ability to deliver high-quality patient care and its business objectives stands a good chance of being compromised.

Around 20–30% of the annual outlays of the NHS are committed to providing and maintaining the estate, which is worth £23 billion, with a replacement value of £72 billion. In England alone, almost £9 billion is spent each year by trusts and health authorities on 'non-pay' items ranging from baked beans and blankets to bandages, syringes, MRI scanners and computer systems.[1] Managing this vast array of property and goods is no small task, and the NHS has invested considerable effort in both modernising its approach to and improving the quality of procurement, operations and disposal.

In parallel with modernisation reforms for clinical services, efficiency initiatives have been introduced for estates, facilities and supplies. NHS Estates, an executive agency of the Department of Health, is charged with developing and promoting this national reform agenda for estates. Its separate and independent partner organisations for supplies are the NHS Purchasing and Supply Agency[2] and the NHS Logistics Authority.[3]

This chapter describes some key developments in this agenda, and demonstrates some practical ways of using information within healthcare organisations to further this agenda. It does not directly address issues related to capital building works or the review and monitoring of the Capital Investment Manual (CIM, formerly CAPRICODE), the mandatory procedural framework that governs the inception, planning, processing and control of individual health building schemes. That topic merits a book in its own right.

The estate and facilities

To deliver a modern NHS, fit for the twenty-first century, buildings and equipment are required that are in the right place, in the right condition, of the right type and which will be able to respond to future service needs. The estates strategy aims to ensure that there are high-quality, well-located buildings, which give best value in facilitating the delivery of modern patient care services.[4]

The 'estate' may be broadly defined as the land on which services are provided, the buildings in which services are housed, the plant and equipment inside those buildings (e.g electricity generators, air-conditioning units, oxygen pipes and X-ray machines), the environment and its amenities (e.g. landscape, wildlife and pollution) and services of a non-clinical nature (e.g. security and fire safety).

The national estates policy and strategy are developed by NHS Estates, with Regional Offices taking on the management and monitoring of performance against national objectives. These are largely concerned with improving efficiency and value for money during the life cycle of NHS assets – through procurement, operational management, the identification of surplus estates and, if appropriate, their disposal, and ensuring that the environment and facilities are safe, secure, comfortable and welcoming for patients and staff.

The performance management philosophy

The NHS Estates performance management philosophy is underpinned by a vision ('a modern environment for the NHS to deliver high-quality healthcare'), a mission ('building better healthcare') and an action model which is very similar to a number of healthcare service quality improvement approaches described in Chapter 7. It is called the European Foundation Quality Management (EFQM) Excellence Model,[5,6] and includes the following:

- a baseline assessment of performance
- identification of operations most in need of improvement and the nature of the improvement required
- comparison of performance and practice with others
- learning from best practice wherever that occurs
- practical action to implement improvements.

It has specified a large number of performance areas to which management focus has been directed, and these are detailed in a range of policy documents, guidelines and manuals, including the following:

1   the NHS Plan,[7] covering such matters as:
    - the elimination of mixed-sex accommodation by 2002
    - 25% of the maintenance backlog from a baseline of April 2000 to be cleared by 2004
    - the physical condition of the estate to be sound and operationally safe by 2005
    - investing so that 40% of the NHS estate is less than 15 years old by 2010.
2   the Capital Investment Manual,[8] covering many aspects of investment practice, including the efficient use of resources such as heat and power, reuse and recycling practices, and innovative purchasing
3   Concode,[9] covering procurement policies for contracting and commissioning
4   Firecode,[10] containing the 1991 Building Regulations and fire safety requirements
5   Estatecode,[11] setting out requirements for estates development and management strategies supported within trusts' business plans
6   NHS guidance on Private Finance Initiatives (PFI)[12]
7   local arrangements for strategic and outline business cases for capital investment, not necessarily from the private sector
8   NHS Health and Safety legislation
9   the Environmental Protection Act
10 Controls Assurance and risk management standards set out in HSC 1999/123, such as management of the asset base
11 review of NHS procurement – implementing the recommendations.[13]

Performance management of the estate at an organisational level

Healthcare providers and organisations need to take these policies, regulations and guidelines and adopt them as the basis for their own estates strategies and performance management programmes within the quality improvement model espoused by NHS Estates. Fortunately for estates and facilities managers in the NHS, NHS Estates has developed and made available an estates strategy framework and performance management and review programme that is outstanding in its comprehensiveness, quality, and ease of use and application.

The estates strategy

Outlined in the national requirements for a health organisation's estates strategy are the following basic parameters for subsequent performance management:

- an analysis of the existing estate, its condition and performance
- priorities for estates improvement, development or disposal
- an investment programme (including capital) for meeting service need, standards (both statutory and non-statutory), reducing backlog maintenance, acquiring new building, and upgrading buildings
- an environmental impact assessment
- a mitigation plan for avoiding any harmful environmental effects
- development control plans
- summary of proposed acquisitions and disposal of land and buildings, and anticipated proceeds
- the way in which the above changes will deliver improvements in estates performance
- a risk management strategy.

Estate performance, including the Estates Returns Information Collection (ERIC)

The estates strategy is the prerequisite for initiating management measures to improve the performance and use of the estate through the analysis of the existing facilities and buildings and their condition. Within the strategy for each trust, it is expected that targets will be established against which the performance of the estate can be monitored. NHS Estates requests that appropriate performance targets be set to measure the following:

- improvements in the quality of the operational estate over time (e.g. reductions in backlog maintenance, annual perception surveys and environment measurement tools)
- improvements in statutory compliance, risk reduction and controls assurance standards[14] (e.g. reduction in incident rates and non-compliance)
- changes in the revenue cost of the operational estate over time (e.g. by mapping trends in overall maintenance costs, utilities costs and the trust's income-to-asset-value ratio against a common base point)
- better use of the estate (e.g. site density, asset value and income ratios)
- better quality of the patient environment (using models such as the patient's journey).

To assist estates performance review and monitoring, NHS Estates has built a series of performance indicators from which each trust can benchmark its estate performance and monitor improvements. The performance indicators aggregate into five groups as follows:

1 space efficiency
2 asset productivity
3 asset redeployment
4 estate quality
5 cost of occupancy.

Each of these groups contains four different performance indicators.

The data from which the performance indicators and benchmarks are drawn comes from the Estates Returns Information Collection (ERIC), a mandatory national analysis of estate information collected via the estate table of the Trust Financial Proformas (TFPs) from all NHS trusts in England.

Until 2000–01, the ERIC software tool was distributed to all trusts to enable data collection, and to give feedback on the previous year's information, including performance indicators benchmarked against comparator trusts. In 2000–01, the data collection moved to a web-base.

Each trust's ERIC data is drawn from a wide range of local

internal data sets (costing data from finance and payroll information systems; adverse incidents from incident reporting systems; patient activity data from patient administration systems; staffing data from personnel systems; service activity data from information systems such as transport, sterilising, hotel and waste management; and patient satisfaction surveys). Data definitions, critical success factors and scoring systems for performance are clearly specified and defined, and allow easy recognition of practical results translated into performance measures such as the following:

- domestic waste cost per tonne
- cleaning cost by area cleaned
- postal costs by occupied floor area
- estate budget by occupied floor area.

Overall, this web-based performance management, monitoring and benchmarking programme for estates is one of the most accessible and comprehensive management tools available in the NHS, and it serves as a model of excellence which should be replicated for clinical quality performance management and review.

A practical example of how the estates strategy framework can be used to baseline present performance, compare it with peer organisations and 'best-in-class' enterprises, and identify gaps and shortfalls in performance is described below.

Estates strategy example

'Fairy' Acute Trust was built in 1935. The existing main building was the first stage of a planned development, but further phases were not completed because of the outbreak of the Second World War. A number of buildings have been converted to offices, but still have basic problems with windows, roofs, heating and utilities. Disruption to traffic and patients is caused when service ducts are accessed. Storage space for supplies and waste in ward areas was not a feature of the original 1935 hospital design, thereby creating unsightly and untidy disposal problems.

The value of the trust's land, buildings and equipment, detailed in the assets register as at April 2000, is as follows:

- land value: £27.5 million

- building value: £102.8 million
- equipment value: £14.4 million.

A summary of its existing estate is shown in Table 3.1.

Table 3.1 Outline of existing estate

Land area (ha) (acres)	38 ha (93)
Building area (m²)	138 000
Year of initial construction	1933
Tenure	Leasehold (999 years from 1933)
Major clinical services	Cardiac; oncology; renal; neurosciences; liver; regional Accident and Emergency/trauma; outpatients; burns and plastic surgery

When preparing its estates strategy, the trust undertook a baseline assessment of the estate across the following five facets:

- physical condition
- functional suitability
- space utilisation
- statutory compliance
- energy performance.

Physical condition

Table 3.2 and Figure 3.1 below indicate that almost 75% of the estate requires investment to bring it to an acceptable condition. Examples of particular concern are defective brickwork due to water seepage, radiators heated by domestic hot water systems in the administration block, and wards with duplicated pipework and inadequate heating systems which are constrained by the building design. The latter problems have occurred because of attempts to replace the original pipework, but have left the trust with a liability.

Table 3.2 Physical condition survey, 1997 and 2000

Category	1997	2000
A (as new)	5.0%	2.7%
B (adequate)	21.0%	20.6%
C (major change needed)	56.0%	58.2%
Cx (uneconomic)	10.0%	12.0%
D (imminent breakdown)	7.0%	4.5%
Dx (replacement needed)	1.0%	1.9%

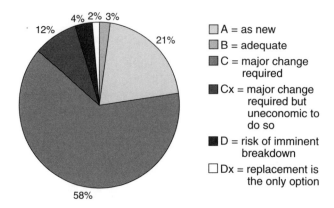

Figure 3.1 Physical condition survey for the year 2000.

Functional suitability

The functional suitability of many parts of the hospital is impaired by the age and layout of existing buildings. A number of wards are of the Nightingale design, which limits their ability to provide patient care to acceptable standards. Physical relationships between departments are poor (e.g. outpatients and diagnostic facilities are at opposite ends of the site). *See* Figure 3.2 and Table 3.3.

Table 3.3 Functional suitability survey, 1997 and 2000

Category	1997	2000
A (ideal)	3.0%	6.2%
B (adequate)	32.0%	31.9%
C (tolerable)	35.0%	34.8%
D (major change)	21.0%	18.5%
Dx (replacement needed)	9.0%	8.5%

Space utilisation

This analysis indicates that 68% of the estate is adequately utilised, with no significant change on this dimension having occurred since 1997.

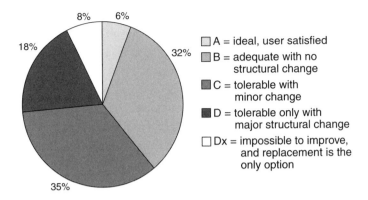

Figure 3.2 Functional suitability survey for the year 2000.

Table 3.4 Space utilisation survey, 1997 and 2000

Category	1997	2000
1 (empty)	6.0%	5.6%
2 (underused)	19.0%	17.0%
3 (adequate)	67.0%	68.0%
4 (overcrowded)	8.0%	9.3%

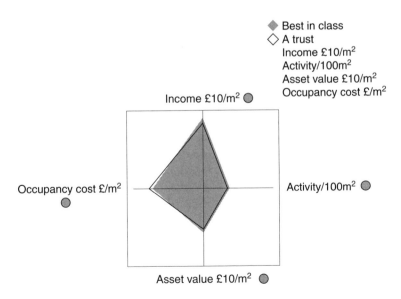

Figure 3.3 Space efficiency, relating the estate and its annual occupancy cost to the output of the trust (2000).

The fine line on the radar chart in Figure 3.3 indicates the trust's performance on this indicator. When compared with the shaded area in the middle of the chart, it shows that there is a slight margin between the two for 'occupancy costs', but an even match on the other attributes. This demonstrates that the trust is generally using floor space efficiently because its income, activity levels and asset values are all sound relative to the gross internal floor area, when compared with similar NHS trusts. 'Fairy' Trust is spending slightly more on occupancy costs compared with 'best–in–class' hospitals. If this expenditure is not reviewed, there may be increasing financial pressures in future years (e.g. from backlog maintenance expenditure requirements or lack of capital for reinvestment from capital charges).

Statutory standards

The current estimate for achieving statutory and safety compliance is £2.3 million. This assessment from the previous 1997 condition survey is under review, to take account of new legislation and risk management approaches. The estimate for fire safety compliance is £1.1 million.

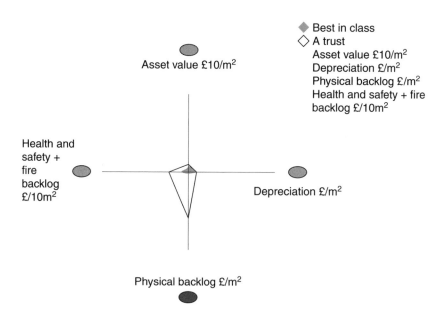

Figure 3.4 Estate quality: the overall condition of the estate relative to value and age.

Three of the four performance indicators in the radar chart in Figure 3.4 indicate poor trust performance against comparable trusts, suggesting that the quality of the estate is below acceptable standards. Concerns centre on the trust's physical condition backlogs, and its capacity to meet Health and Safety and fire safety standards.

Energy performance

The trust has achieved the national target of a 20% real-terms reduction in energy consumption from a baseline in 1990–91. However, its overall energy performance is category C (tolerable), because although its Combined Heat and Power facility reduces the overall utilities costs, it also increases the energy consumption. This is compounded by poor heating controls, inadequate insulation and the original single-glazed metal-frame windows in many buildings.

Financial analysis of five-facet survey

The costs of bringing the overall estate infrastructure to condition 'B' (defined as 'sound, operationally safe and exhibits only minor deterioration') are £88.1 million – up from £71.8 million in 1997.

Performance indicators

Estate strategy performance indicators are designed to allow in-formed judgement on the efficiency and condition of the NHS estate compared with peer hospitals. They are expressed as a ratio of cost or activity (finished consultant episodes) to buildings and land areas.

A 'traffic-light' system classifies performance management infor-mation into the following three categories:

- green ▫ – no or very limited problems, indicating performance within 'best of class'
- amber ▪ – acceptable performance, but with room for improve-ment
- red ■ – serious concerns due to poor performance.

Table 3.5 illustrates 'Fairy' Acute Trust's performance indicator scores compared with those similar NHS trusts.

Table 3.5 'Fairy' Trust's performance 1999–2000

Performance indicator summary	Trust PI score	Comparable cluster performance indicator bands		
		33%	34%	33%
Space efficiency				
Income £10/m²	148	88	89 and 109	110+
Activity/100m²	68	48	49 and 61	62+
Asset value £10/m²	105	71	72 and 83	84+
Occupancy cost £/m²	144	117	118 and 134	135+
Asset productivity				
Asset value £10/m²	105	71	72 and 83	84+
Capital charges £/m²	116	84	85 and 104	105+
Total backlog £/m²	637	41	42 and 142	143+
Rent and rates £/10m²	76	88	89 and 110	111+
Asset deployment				
Land £/m²	199	43	44 and 68	69+
Building £10/m²	74	56	57 and 69	70+
Equipment £/m²	104	75	76 and 111	112+
Capital charges £/m²	116	84	85 and 104	105+
Estate quality				
Asset value £10/m²	105	71	72 and 83	84+
Depreciation £/m²	57	42	43 and 46	47+
Physical backlog £/m²	614	41	42 and 142	143+
Health and Safety plus fire backlog £/10m²	230	66	67 and 293	294+
Cost of occupancy				
Rent and rates £/10m²	76	88	89 and 110	111+
Energy/utility £/10m²	81	70	71 and 93	94+
Maintenance costs £/10m²	151	123	124 and 145	146+
Capital charges £/m²	116	84	85 and 104	105+

Summary of performance assessment

The baseline assessment, performance indicators and radar charts demonstrate the following.

- The trust's income level of £148 $\times$ 10/m² is among the best in class. This reflects the specialist nature of the services provided.
- The activity level of 68 finished consultant episodes/100m² is also high.
- Rent and rates are low at £76/10m², due to the age and condition of the buildings.
- The land value at £199/m² is high, reflecting the extent of the trust's undeveloped land and the locality in comparison with the cluster group.

- The maintenance and backlog figure of £859/m² is very high, due to the age and condition of the estate, when the range for the cluster is £121 to £450/m².

The performance indicators suggest that the asset base is near the end of its design life, and is in need of investment and rationalisation to achieve a more modern and functionally suitable estate. There are also strong indications that the quality of the estate is generally below acceptable standards. This is supported by the five-facet survey.

Supplies

The proper management of supplies is essential to the efficiency and effectiveness of clinical and support services. Patient care depends on the assured availability of high-quality equipment, materials and services. A Cabinet Office review of NHS procurement in mid-1999 found that 80% of trusts had no annual savings target and no agreed strategy for procurement. With this in mind, the NHS Purchasing and Supply Agency was created for England in April 2000, with the following brief:

- to co-ordinate and guide NHS procurement policy and strategy
- to develop and improve the national purchasing function, and explore the scope for mandatory national contracts
- to provide expertise to trusts and health authorities on procurement matters
- to develop common procurement terms and conditions
- to collate and disseminate information on procurement for benchmarking
- to maintain a market overview of procurement and advise NHS organisations on market issues.

A number of recommendations emerged from this review which must now be given effect in trusts and health authorities. These are set out clearly in HSC 1999/143.

A supplies strategy

Now in its second year of operation, the NHS Purchasing and Supply Agency has an ambitious development agenda. During 2000, it reviewed all trusts' supply strategies, ensuring the application of a common methodology. During the period 2000–02, it has set itself a number of key tasks, including the following:

- reviewing supply management arrangements with a view to agreeing appropriate levels of purchasing activities – at national, consortium or local level
- establishing jointly with the NHS Logistics Authority a strategy and action plan for delivering a modern, integrated, cost-effective supply chain for the NHS
- with the Audit Commission, establishing revised key performance measures and indicators.

From the perspective of operational supply managers, the provision of national benchmarks of performance, developed and circulated electronically as now occurs with estates management, would be greatly welcomed. In the meantime, the existing core performance indicators are those specified in HSC 1999/143 (*see* Table 3.7 on page 55).

Performance management of supplies at an organisational level

As with estates, the big NHS modernisation agenda has placed demands on trusts to performance manage their supplies and the processes underpinning their procurement and dispersal to operational areas. Each organisation's corporate and business objectives must include sub-objectives and actions designed to promote efficient procurement as well as delivery of a quality end-product to users. Nothing so confounds and irritates operational staff and clinicians as shortages of supplies, or late delivery of stores.

> **Example 3.1** St Anthony's Teaching Hospital Trust
>
> 'St Anthony's' Teaching Hospital Trust has reviewed its high cancellation rates in renal and cardiac surgery (16% and 42%, respectively) over a six-month period up to November 2000. These cancellation rates have led to significant under-performance on inpatient activity contracts in these specialities, with a resultant clawing back of income by the health authority. A number of factors contributed to this position, the most important ones being the supply and utilisation of ITU and downstream ward beds. The review revealed one surprise contributory factor, namely poor stock control of theatre supplies of small but important items. Overhaul of this ordering and supplies chain has, in its own right, reduced the rate of operative procedure cancellation rates by 27%.

As with all aspects of performance management, the key starting point is the supply strategy and its objectives. In designing a supply strategy, each trust will need to take into account a number of key performance areas:

1 how patient care is affected by best practice management of supplies
2 the scope of its supply strategy, such as:
    • what is handled in-house or outsourced
    • non-pay expenditure on items such as pharmaceuticals, pathology, IT
    • non-pay expenditure on services such as outsourced contract management
    • information needs and reporting levels
    • physical distribution
    • payment systems
3 the need for the supply strategy to integrate with other related trust activities such as environmental, human resources and health and safety arrangements
4 the ways in which the supply strategy will support other corporate objectives, such as estates management, inter-trust partnerships and cost improvement programmes
5 decision-making delegations with respect to matters such as outsourcing, acquisition, tendering, contracting and expenditure limits
6 the level and balance of supplies collaboration nationally and locally through national contracts, national logistics service/ provision of goods and local testing of national or specialised arrangements
7 expectations of staff and suppliers' behaviour in terms of public accountability and commitment to statutory and mandatory regulations (e.g. standing orders, financial instructions and procurement regulations)
8 policy or intentions for e-commerce
9 the need for information and reporting to the Board, and the style and content of the performance management supporting the strategy.

An illustration of a work plan against such strategy objectives is described below.

Performance objectives for a supplies strategy

'St Timothy's' Trust has developed a supply strategy to improve the management of its £72.4 million non-pay annual budget. For many years in this trust, delegated purchasing and ordering activity has been undertaken by local departments, leading to a proliferation of procedures, lack of standardisation of products, and duplication of manpower. During 2000–01, it wishes to centralise its contracting activity through the Supplies Department, capturing key information on an Access database, supported by project management software, to ensure that appropriate resources are allocated to the renewal of existing contract commitments and to assist planning for the inclusion of additional contracting initiatives.

To allow the trust to assess current performance of local purchasing, and pending the development of national benchmarks, it has initiated the sharing of local procurement benchmarking data with two other comparable trusts that have corresponding Regional specialties. It has invested heavily in its finance computer systems, and has developed an electronic purchase order facility. It is proud of this development, and believes that it has become a national leader in this field.

It wishes to develop a single-site theatre store within its Sterile Services Department warehouse, using the computer stock inventory management module of its finance system. It plans to service all 22 theatres from a single-site theatre store within the next six months, and will then extend the service to intensive critical-care areas, radiology, catering, domestics and estates stores. The trust is currently reviewing its need for additional storage facilities to deal with this expansion.

It has created a Capital Equipping Manager post in recognition of the need to develop 'in-house' expertise to deal with the supplies requirements of both existing and future capital schemes. To assist in the selection of medical equipment, the trust has established a Medical Equipment Group with clear terms of reference which recognise the need for standardisation. It also subscribes to a service which includes a worldwide database of medical equipment to assist in sourcing and evaluation. This database is made available to relevant trust staff who would benefit from the information. As part of the selection process within the trust's Capital Replacement Programme, this database service provider will aid assessment of the budget costing to maximise capital resources.

The trust has already identified the need to assess the environmental impact of purchasing decisions, and it has incorporated these in the decision-making process as part of the standard documentation in its supplies tenders.

The trust's strategy has been structured to meet its obligations under HSC 1999/143 and the Cabinet Office Review, and has set the following objectives:

- to achieve 3% savings annually on influenced non-pay expenditure (those items over which direct influence is difficult include business rates, depreciation, insurance, and clinical negligence provisions)
- to maximise materials management
- to increase influence and control over non-pay expenditure by professional supply management
- to improve understanding of where, why and with which suppliers expenditure is made, and to reduce the supplier base and product mix
- to ensure value for money by reviewing 'make, buy or lease' decisions and undertaking benchmarking analyses.

Its process/milestones measures for these goals are listed in Table 3.6. Having developed these local process measures of performance, the trust will need to ensure that they are supplemented with the quantitative measures recommended in HSC 1999/143, shown in Table 3.7. Review of performance on these objectives will be undertaken quarterly, in a process similar to that described in Chapter 7.

Table 3.6 Strategy objectives and process measures

Objective	Process measure
1 Contribute to trust's savings target on influenced non-pay expenditure of 3% per annum	• Identify and produce evidence to support savings initiatives taken. Categorise into appropriate areas
2 Maximise materials management	• Identify remaining potential sites to extend materials management. Produce costed implementation plan and complete roll-out • Establish a single-site theatre store • Roll out to 22 theatres • Roll out to other identified areas
3 Increase influence over and control of non-pay expenditure by professional supply management	• Agree areas to be influenced, and increase supplies control to 100% • Develop the contract database and work plan on a 3-year rolling programme basis • Produce management reports for procurement staff to strengthen efficient resource use; identify process and quality assurance milestones for reports; train staff in structured project management techniques using reports • Conduct trend analysis of spend across products/divisions/suppliers • Establish the Supplies Policy Review Group • Investigate solutions to procurement issues (including information technology) that can demonstrate process improvements and generate regular management feedback • Improve the speed of requisition throughput by using trust-specific catalogues • Undertake a cost-benefit analysis of the use of purchasing cards
4 Improve understanding of where, why and with which suppliers expenditure is made – increase control and significantly reduce the supplier base and product mix	• Explore the potential of strategic supplier partnerships • Introduce innovative schemes with suppliers that challenge conventional thinking and deliver tangible benefits to trust
5 Ensure value for money by reviewing make, buy or lease decisions, and undertaking benchmarking analysis	• Review and strengthen quality initiatives to enhance the contribution of procurement staff

Table 3.7 Key supplies performance indicators and measures

Key indicator definition and notes	Specification of measure
Supply 'influence' and control is where money spent on non-pay goods and services is covered by formal purchasing arrangements as follows: • goods from NHS Supplies Wholesaling Division • NHS Supplies purchasing contracts • goods/services competitively tendered and contracted for by the trust	• Show percentage of non-pay expenditure in each trust department (pharmacy, pathology, radiology, theatres, catering, estates included) covered by the same categories • Show how much (percentage) of the value of their goods and services is secured through each of the three same categories • Carry out regular benchmarking of performance against other trusts at local and national level

Purchasing savings achieved
Plans for achieving savings will be agreed with Divisions/Trust Management Board
	• Show breakdown by agreed category by division:
	  (i) 3% national contribution
	  (ii) Trust Cost Improvement Programmes (CIPs)
	  (iii) Supplies Department initiatives further broken down into recurring savings reductions in stock-holding, identifying other potential savings not realised

Product rationalisation and clinical involvement *There is a need to balance the issue of individual product preference and product quality, with issues of unnecessary transaction and variety costs. Measures can be used to identify current position and to 'optimise' this balance*	• Identify the number of different consumable products in use within specific trust departments (product lines) • Identify the number of projects under way to review/trial alternative products and 'rationalise' on use • Identify the degree of involvement of clinical staff on each project, showing the names and type of involvement
Level of influence and control of non-pay expenditure by professional supply management. *Non-pay expenditure includes all goods, services and capital equipment, including pharmacy and pathology supplies*	• Using the TFR3 structure, show the percentage of expenditure covered by each of the three routes described in the left-hand column • Show the top 100 suppliers by value and percentage influence according to the same three categories
Reduction in the number of low-value purchases *Low-value purchases are usually defined as less than £100. They are of interest because the costs of processing such orders very often exceed the value of them*	• Show the number and value of low-value purchases, by department and by supplier • Show the total time and total cost of processing low-value orders in the trust • Undertake a trend analysis of changes to performance, with commentary on the possible reasons for variation, such as introduction of purchasing card

Cont.

Table 3.7 Key supplies performance indicators and measures (cont.)

Key indicator definition and notes	Specification of measure
Rationalisation of the number of suppliers used *This measure is concerned with the number of active suppliers used, and it seeks to indicate change in the number and range of transactions and relationships*	• Select appropriate periods for comparisons • Indicate the total annual spend with each supplier • Track changes to volume and value of purchase order transactions resulting from rationalisation • Indicate timing of actions designed to effect such changes
Service quality/stakeholder satisfaction *The purpose of this measure is to assess alignment of professional supply activity with trust objectives, and to help to identify performance issues (both positive and negative)*	Regular user/stakeholder satisfaction questionnaire to be analysed and presented (NHS Supplies has considerable experience in undertaking such surveys in conjunction with external advisers, and can provide guidance)
Price trend analysis *The purpose of this measure is to help to assess purchasing performance on prices paid for goods and services*	For the top 100 products by value, show price paid over time (monthly), with reasons for variations
Cost inflation resistance *The purpose of this is to help to assess performance in resisting supplier attempts to increase prices*	For the trust's top 100 suppliers by value, show for each selected period: • the number of suppliers notifying requests for price increases • the number of requests challenged by the trust • the number of successful challenges by the trust (zero increases) • the number of unsuccessful challenges by the trust
Variations in usage and use of equipment *The purpose of this measure is to use 'average' performance to identify possible 'outliers' in terms of consumption of consumables, or use of equipment. 'Outliers' may be related to a particular context, or may indicate performance issues. It is also useful to record the potential for equipment pooling*	• Select a range of 'standard' consumables for comparison between trust departments • Undertake internal benchmarking involving patient activity, clinical practice and usage patterns • Identify the causes of significant variation in consumption • Identify the type of equipment held and the number of departments reliant on equipment pool
Extent of materials management cover *Materials management refers to the supply chain from supplier to end user, and the extent to which the flow of materials can be enhanced and transactions reduced using automated stock control and replenishment*	• Show the number of items on materials management systems • Show the value of purchases on materials management systems compared with the total value of purchases • Show the number of departments within trust with materials management service covering over 50% of their supplies activity

Key indicator definition and notes	Specification of measure
Purchasing performance and control *The purpose of this measure is to help to monitor the focus and priorities of supply. To be manageable, this measure should be concerned with all purchase orders above £5000.*	In relation to significant value orders (and shown by supplier, trust department and value) indicate: • the percentage covered by formal contract or not • the percentage covered by competitive tender/quotation or single tender action, with justification for single tender action
Workload measures *The purpose of these measures is to quantify certain aspects of operational performance of the supply stream within various departments of the trust and, over time, to review or target change in these performance factors. These measures will need to be recorded within the supplies department manually or using appropriate software packages available on the purchase order system*	For defined periods, report: • the number of requisitions received by the department • the 'dwell time' of requisitions (the number of days between receipt of requisition and the order being placed) • the number of purchase orders raised by the department • the average number of lines per order • average value of purchase orders raised
Other specified measures required by the Director of Finance	• The number of single tender action requests and reasons broken down by division • Invoice queries by category

Source: Core indicators, as recommended in HSC 1999/143.

EU Procurement Rules

The EU Procurement Rules apply to public authorities, including NHS authorities and trusts. The purpose of these rules is to harmonise procedures for the award of contracts above a certain value across the EU, and to ensure the free movement of goods and services within the EU and therefore increase opportunities for suppliers and contractors. In most cases this requires competition.

The regulations set out a process to be followed, provide detailed criteria for specification, selection and award of contracts, and specify timings for certain stages of the process.

The rules apply to the procurement of supplies, services and works above the thresholds shown in Table 3.8. The thresholds are reassessed in January of alternate years.[15]

They are based on the principle that procurement decisions should achieve value for money through competition, and they are designed to avoid discrimination on the grounds of origin of supplier. They aim to ensure that all suppliers and contractors are treated equally.

Table 3.8 EU procurement thresholds

Supplies	£144 456 excluding VAT
Services	£144 456 excluding VAT
Works	£3 611 395 excluding VAT

The thresholds apply:

- when a single purchase exceeds the threshold
- when a 'call-off' contract is let to purchase goods with a total value over the threshold
- for regular supply contracts where the aggregate is likely to exceed the threshold. This covers a series of contracts with a supplier for the provision of products of the same type.

There are then three types of award procedure:

- *open* – where all interested persons can tender
- *restricted* – where only selected persons may submit tenders
- *negotiated* – where a purchaser may negotiate the terms of the contract with one or more selected persons.

NHS authorities and trusts can choose between open and restricted procedures, but can only use the negotiated procedures in limited circumstances.

The procedure is as follows.

- The organisation undertaking the procurement must give all suppliers the opportunity to tender by placing a tender notice in the *Official Journal of the European Communities* (OJEC Notice).
- Invite tenders in accordance with prescribed procedures and timings. The timings can be accelerated by publication of a Prior Information Notice (PIN).
- The organisation must ensure that all specifications comply with regulations covering standards and do not discriminate against suppliers.
- Specify in the tender notice the technical and financial basis on which suppliers will be assessed.
- Follow the criteria for award of contract.
- Publish the results of the contract award by placing a notice in the *OJEC*, and debrief unsuccessful suppliers if requested.

- Provide annual returns.

If the rules are not followed, an unsuccessful tenderer can make a challenge which could end up in the High Courts. Damages may be awarded. The unsuccessful tenderer does not have to show that they would have won the contract had the rules been applied. They merely need to demonstrate that the rules were not applied.

The future for the performance management of the estate and supplies

There is clear Government recognition that much of the NHS estate is 'tired' and unfit for its purpose. It needs refreshing and overhaul, and funds are now coming on stream, either from the Exchequer or through the Private Finance Initiative, to rebuild and refurbish in order to deliver a contemporary health system comparable with the very best in other developed health economies. Similarly, there is an imperative to learn from private industry and to adopt the most up-to-date methods of managing the supply chain, not only to deliver financial efficiencies, but also to improve support for clinical operations in order to deliver high-quality healthcare.

With regard to the estate and supplies, it is not easy to predict the impact of future advances in technology, engineering and science, but we can be assured that they will be significant, and that they will greatly influence the shape and design of future healthcare provision. For some of these new directions, the planning and lead times are likely to be protracted.

Government's purpose is to create an intelligent infrastructure – vision, philosophy, practical methods, adaptability and flexibility – to work in the here and now to upgrade and better manage NHS assets and to prepare for the future. Through NHS Estates and the NHS Purchasing and Supply Agency, this infrastructure is being put in place. Performance management will be a key tool in realising these aspirations.

> **Key points**
>
> - The management of NHS estates, facilities and supplies is undergoing national redevelopment on a large scale in innovative and imaginative ways.
> - NHS Estates has developed a web-based national performance management and benchmarking service for estates and facilities that is second to none in its comprehensiveness, relevance, utility and ease of use.
> - With this service, operational estates and facilities managers will be assisted enormously within their own organisations, although they will need to ensure that their local information systems which feed into this national data collection are robust and accurate.
> - On the supplies front, the NHS Purchasing and Supply Agency is playing 'catch-up', and will be developing a parallel set of national performance benchmarks covering supplies.
> - The push for e-commerce will accelerate these supply developments.

References

1   Merry PM (ed.) (2000) *Wellard's NHS Handbook 2000–01.* JMH Publishing, London.
2   www.pasa.doh.gov.uk
3   www.logistics.nhs.uk
4   NHS Estates (1999) *Developing an Estates Strategy.* The Stationery Office, London.
5   NHS Estates (2001) *Building Better Healthcare: presentation portfolio.* The Stationery Office, London.
6   British Quality Foundation (2000) *The Model in Practice: using the EFQM Excellence Model to deliver continuous improvement.* British Quality Foundation, London.
7   NHS Executive (2000) *The National Plan for the New NHS. The new NHS: the need for change.* The Stationery Office, London.
8   NHS Executive (2000) *Capital Investment Manual.* The Stationery Office, London.
9   NHS Estates (2000) *Concode.* The Stationery Office, London.
10 NHS Estates (2000) *Firecode.* The Stationery Office, London.
11 NHS Estates (2000) *Estatecode.* The Stationery Office, London.
12 NHS (1999) *Public Private Partnerships in the NHS: the private finance initiative.* The Stationery Office, London.
13 HSC 1999/143. *Review of NHS Procurement. Implementing the recommendations.* Department of Health, London.
14 http://tap.ccta.gov.uk/doh/rm5.nsf/AdminDocs/CAStandards
15 http://www.doh.gov.uk/purchasing/procedures.htm

4 Managing finance to maximise health gain

Introduction

Finance makes it possible to ensure a workforce fit to provide health services and to ensure that they have the premises, equipment and other supplies they need to do their job. In this chapter we shall look at the sources of finance, the way in which finance is allocated to healthcare organisations, and some aspects of managing finance within healthcare organisations.

These matters are subject to a wide range of financial regulations and requirements with which all organisations must comply.

There is a great deal more to the management of finance than merely ensuring that the books are balanced at the end of the year and that the regulations have been complied with. Finance is perhaps the most powerful driver of change and influence on behaviour of Government, commissioners and providers of healthcare. This section will attempt to look at the ways in which the methods of allocating and managing finance can either help or hinder an organisation in achieving its objectives.

Sources of finance

The Government's comprehensive spending review, announced in July 1998, outlined a three-year settlement for public expenditure rather than the one-year finance cycle that had been applied previously.

Table 4.1 shows the NHS health authority revenue resource limits for the single year of 2000–2001 for England.

Table 4.1 Health authority revenue resource limits

	£ million for 2000–01
HCFHS current budget*	41 465
Capital charge and other funding adjustments	1492
Total available	42 957
Deployed as:	
Centrally funded initiatives and services and special allocations	5880
Total for health authorities	37 077
Of which:	
Performance fund	100
Cost of living supplement	65
Health inequalities adjustment	130

* Hospital, community and family health services.

The way in which allocations are made has varied over the years and reflects changes in the following:

- the structure of the organisation

- the financial information required

- the use of the allocation process to achieve central objectives.

The figures presented above are somewhat obscured by land sales, recycled NHS debt, the modernisation fund and the Private Finance Initiative (PFI).

The NHS is financed almost entirely from general taxation and National Insurance contributions, with a variety of minor sources of funding from charitable funds, patient charges, land sales, etc. In 1999–2000 it was estimated that 79% would come from general taxation and 13% from the NHS element of the National Insurance contributions. The sources are summarised in Table 4.2.

Table 4.2 Sources of funding

Source of funding	Amount (for 2000–01)
Total funding	£47 845 million
Total public funding	89.6%
General taxation	77.7%
NHS element of National Insurance contributions	11.98%
Total from other sources	10.4%
Charges	1.9 %
Capital refunds	5.1%
Miscellaneous	3.4%

Source: The Government's Expenditure Plans 2000/2001; http://www.doh.gov.uk/dohreport/report2000/dr2000–03.html

Further sources of funding

The Road Traffic (NHS Charges) Act (1999) introduced charges to recoup in full the cost of the NHS treating road-traffic victims. This scheme came into operation in April 1999 and was expected to raise £16.5 million during the nine months up to the end of 1999.

The National Lotteries Act created a new good cause, namely the New Opportunities Fund, which provides funding for health, education and the environment. The fund aims to support targeted initiatives committing £300 million within the UK. One of the first initiatives was to establish a network of 'healthy living' centres offering fitness checks, fitness routines and advice on diet and lifestyle. A further £150 million has been made available from the same source to fund cancer prevention, detection, treatment and care.

Funding comparisons

According to Treasury sources, total health spending will rise to 7.6% of the gross domestic product (GDP) by 2003–04. This compares with a current European average of around 8%, and figures of 9.6% in France, 10.7% in Germany and 13.9% in the US.

Financial allocation

Allocations changing behaviour

The way in which the 2000–01 allocations were targeted showed a clear intention to change the behaviour of local health services and to achieve national priorities.

In the Secretary of State for Health's announcement of the health authority resource limits for 2001–02, there were measures aimed at improving performance – to reward success rather than to bail out failure. A £100 million Performance Fund was allocated. The 'best' local services would be free to spend their share of the fund on equipment, facilities or cash bonuses for staff. The 'worst' local services would get their share of the fund, but it would be held by the Modernisation Agency who would use it to target external assistance and help to turn round performance.

Further targeted allocations had the following aims:

- to tackle Government priorities regarding specific diseases (cancer and coronary heart disease) (£450 million)
- to address health inequalities (£130 million)
- to encourage recruitment through a cost-of-living allowance for staff working in the highest-cost parts of the country (£65 million).

Background to allocations

The principles underlying resource allocation were established at the foundation of the NHS in 1945. The aim of the NHS was to achieve as nearly as possible a uniform standard of service for all. This implied that resources should be distributed to ensure equal access to health services for all individuals at equal risk, wherever they live. Over the years, various attempts have been made to ensure that this is achieved by an objective method that could be derived from readily available information and that could be easily understood. Despite various attempts at formulae, inequalities in resource distribution are widely believed to have persisted. There have been various attempts to rectify this situation.

The *Crossman formula* was introduced in the early 1970s by the then Secretary of State, the late Richard Crossman. Revenue funds were distributed on the basis of measures such as population served, number of beds provided and number of cases dealt with. The aim was to eliminate inequalities over a period of ten years. However, after three years very little had changed.

In 1975, the then Secretary of State set up the *Resource Allocation Working Party (RAWP)* with the aim of reviewing the means of distribution of capital and revenue and devising a method of distribution that would be based on relative need. The recommendations of this group were published in 1976 and became the established means of distributing funds to Regional Health Authorities. The RAWP adopted five main criteria that were regarded as indicating relative need:

- size of population
- population age/gender structure
- morbidity
- cost-weighting – relative cost of providing care across regions

- cross-boundary flows – patients resident in one authority obtaining treatment in another.

There were practical problems with regard to obtaining the information needed to calculate the RAWP targets. Data on population size and structure were readily available, and weightings to reflect demand made by each age/gender group could be easily calculated. The measurement of morbidity created real problems. The RAWP decided to use standardised mortality ratios as a proxy. Cost details did not exist at all, and were derived from an analysis of overall cost statements. Statistical data on cross-boundary flows for hospital inpatients were available from the Hospital Activity Analysis, which resulted in the calculation of 'catchment' populations, but no such data were available for outpatients. Little notice would be taken of cross-boundary flows until improved information systems were introduced as a result of the Körner Reports that were published in 1982, 1984 and 1985. Application of the RAWP formula resulted in target allocations being determined. Movement towards these targets recognised that there are practical limits to the amount of reduction that any over-target organisation could achieve within a year, or to the amount that an under-target organisation could spend in a year in order to reduce inequality. It was therefore recommended that redistribution should be achieved over a number of years. There were two main criticisms of RAWP.

- It was only concerned with the redistribution of money, and did not consider such matters as the relative quality of estate or equipment from differing levels of prior investment or the ability to move staff.
- There were concerns about the formula itself and the quality of the information for calculating targets.

Over the years the formulae were refined in an attempt to reflect the healthcare needs of individual areas. In 1991, the RAWP was replaced, and funding to regions and health authorities was allocated through various capital and revenue budgets.

Under the NHS and Community Care Act (1990), GP fundholders received their budgets based on the size of their patient lists. These were used to purchase services for their patients. Health authorities received their budgets based on the population within a given geographical area. In the early stages, after making funding commitments to fundholders, some health authorities had insufficient funds to meet their commitments to the remaining population. Despite the aims of more responsive local services and improved equality, in many places the opposite occurred.

The introduction of primary care groups (PCGs) and primary care trusts (PCTs) has been associated with major changes in funding. Since 1999, the vast majority of the English allocation has been distributed through health authorities in unified budget allocations. The aim of this change was to break down some of the artificial boundaries between hospital and primary care funding. These allocations are passed down to PCGs and PCTs to cover the costs of GPs' staff, premises, computer systems and prescribing, and to commission hospital services. Bringing prescribing into the cash-limited unified budget is an attempt to control this high expenditure.

In addition to the unified budget, health authorities also administer a non-cash-limited family health services budget which covers allowances and fees charged by GPs and payments to opticians, dentists and pharmacists.

Revenue allocations

Following the abolition of Regional Health Authorities, revenue allocations were distributed to health authorities on the basis of *weighted capitation formulae*. A detailed description can be found in the *Health Authority Cash Limits Exposition Book*.[1] The 2001–02 book is the sixth in a series of annual publications, and represents the third year of unified allocations.

Health authority allocations are the main part of their expenditure. They are given allocations for hospital and community health services (HCHS) so that they can commission care for their resident population. In partnership with GPs and in consultation with other agencies and local people, individual health authorities decide on the level and type of services commissioned. In so doing they are required to take into account local circumstances and national and local policies and priorities.

The criteria that affect the general allocation that a health Authority receives are as follows:

- a weighted capitation target set according to the national weighted capitation formula
- the health authority's current allocation

- the distance from target (DFT)
- the speed of change at which the gap is to be closed.

Box 4.1 Weighted capitation target

The following steps are involved in calculation of the weighted capitation target.
1 Crude populations are weighted for age-related need. These populations are multiplied by the relevant expenditure per head, added together and normalised back to the national total population to give crude populations weighted for age.
2 Four needs indices are calculated, namely acute, non-community psychiatric, community psychiatric and community. Each of these is multiplied in turn by the crude populations, normalised and then weighted by the appropriate programme weight.
3 Crude populations are weighted for geographical costs.
4 These weighted populations are used to calculate weighted capitation shares, which are then converted into monetary values:
   - indices are calculated for each of the three adjustments within the formula
   - weighted capitation shares are calculated by multiplying the crude populations by each of the individual indices
   - the crude populations weighted for age, need and geographical area are converted to monetary values to give weighted capitation targets.

In addition to the general allocation, there are some areas where special allocations are made. A weighted capitation approach is used for the following:

- GP staff, premises and computing
- joint finance for collaborative projects with Social Services
- AIDS prevention
- drug misuse.

Special allocations not covered by a formula include provision for the following:

- GP out-of-hours services
- AIDS treatment and care
- elderly long-stay patients.

Capital allocations

The position with regard to capital allocations is somewhat more confused than that for revenue allocations. This confusion arises from the inclusion in the figures of land sale receipts and investment generated through the Private Finance Initiative. The Government's expenditure plans are published each year in the Department of

Health Report. The figures here are from the 2000 Report (presented in April 2000).[2]

The capital investment is targeted towards modernising the infrastructure of the NHS through expenditure on new hospitals, plant and equipment.

Planned NHS capital spending on hospital and community health services (HCHS) is shown in Table 4.3.

Table 4.3 Planned NHS capital spending

Category	£ million for 2000–01
Government spending	1708
Receipts from land sales	363
Private Finance Initiative investment	710
Other NHS spending	32
Total	2813

Of the total, £168 million was specifically earmarked to fund the following priorities:

- reductions in waiting-lists and waiting-times (£90 million)
- renal services (£10 million)
- cancer (£30 million)
- pathology (£15 million)
- coronary heart disease (£20 million)
- ambulance response times (£3 million).

Using the general capital allocations, Regional Offices were specifically charged to address the following:

- elimination of mixed-sex ward accommodation
- compliance with fire safety and other statutory requirements
- compliance with the Disability Discrimination Act
- compliance with best practice on decontamination facilities against variant CJD
- investment to help Health Action Zones to achieve their agreed objectives.

> **Box 4.2** Health Action Zones
>
> These are partnerships between the NHS, local authorities, the voluntary and private sectors and local communities. The Health Action Zones initiative brings together organisations within and beyond the NHS to develop and implement a locally agreed strategy for improving the health of local people.
> Source: http://www.doh.gov.uk/pricare/haz.htm

Rationing: determining investment priorities

In a cash-limited service funded by taxation, rationing is inevitable. Supply is limited by the cash limit, whereas demand is unlimited. This raises the following related questions.

- How should services be rationed?
- How should priorities for investment be decided?

NHS Plan Consultation

In 2000, the UK Government undertook what was considered by many to be 'the largest ever public consultation exercise on health-care services', at a cost to the UK taxpayer of £500 000. The aim was to find out public priorities for spending an additional £20 billion over four years, which the Government promised to allocate.

This exercise consisted of four elements.

- *Workshops*. Two one-day workshops were held involving approximately 100 people representing a 'typical mix of the population'. Those involved discussed the national NHS Plan, voted on key issues and made recommendations for modernisation action teams who had the remit for implementing the plan.

- *Focus groups*. There were ten groups involving approximately 80 people. Each group drew participants from a particular section of the population, the aim being to provide a range of different perspectives.

- *NHS census*. A total of 12 million leaflets with a Freepost reply slip were made available in a wide range of places (e.g. in supermarkets, hospitals and doctors' surgeries). The leaflets asked for 'the top three things that you think would make the NHS better for you and your family', as well as the respondent's age, sex, postcode, and whether the reply was from a member of the public or NHS staff.

- *Service user organisations*. A series of seminars were held with patient organisations by the health minister. In addition, telephone interviews were conducted with 30 of the main patient and user organisations.

The 'census' attracted the most criticism, as is shown by the extract from the *Daily Telegraph* report in Box 4.3.

Box 4.3 £500 000 public NHS census 'a useless PR stunt'

The Government spent yesterday justifying the expenditure of taxpayers' money on a public consultation exercise on the future of the National Health Service to which it already knows the answers.

. . .

The Government said the public consultation would help in the drawing up of the new national plan for the health service, to be published later this year. But the public's concerns – waiting-lists and staff shortages – are already known through polls and focus group surveys.

Nevertheless, Alan Milburn, the Health Secretary, was hailing the survey as a 'once in a lifetime' opportunity, allowing people in England to have their views heard. Opposition parties labelled it as a useless and expensive PR stunt, and there were questions in the marketing industry yesterday about the value of the exercise.

Neil Tweedie, *Daily Telegraph*, 1 June 2000

Oregon Rationing Plan

Perhaps the most well-known public consultation exercise was that carried out by the Oregon Health Services Commission on services to be funded by Medicaid. In 1989, the state of Oregon aimed to define a package of health services that would be provided to all state residents who were on Medicaid. This required health services to be prioritised in order to determine what would be covered and what would not. A Health Services Commission was set up, consisting of primary care physicians, a public health nurse, a social worker and four 'consumers'. Their task was to produce a list of healthcare services ranked in order of priority according to the comparative benefits of each service to the population being served.

The Commission divided the list into condition–treatment pairs (e.g. acute appendicitis–appendectomy). They then attempted to measure the level of clinical effectiveness of each pair by setting up panels of physicians from every specialty. They also assessed how much each treatment affected the patient's quality of life. They then calculated a cost-effectiveness value for each pair. They conducted numerous public meetings and sought opinions from a wide range of service-user groups. The final outcome was a priority list of 709 condition–treatment pairs ranked in order of priority. The cost of providing each pair to the population of Oregon was then calculated. Based on the cost and available money, a line was drawn on the list after the 587th condition–treatment pair. Any treatment below the line was not covered.

The single list produced many counter-intuitive results and some that were considered absurd. For example, lifesaving procedures such as appendectomies were sometimes ranked below less critical ones such as tooth capping.[3] For this reason, the Commission created 17 categories within which condition–treatment pairs were classified. With this modification, all lifesaving therapies were ranked high. However, this still left some problems. For example, because life-saving therapy was ranked high, expensive treatments that postponed the death of terminally ill patients gained a higher priority than effective non-lifesaving therapies. Other problems exist with the methodology, including the use of the Quality of Well-Being (QWB) scale to measure cost-effectiveness.

The success of the Oregon scheme must lie in engaging the public in the debate over what services should be provided and what should not, and in gaining significant public support for the rationing process.

Quality-adjusted life years (QALYs)

The QALY aims to provide an objective measure of the impact or benefit of healthcare interventions on the health of the population. It is based on the principle that a year of poor health is of less value than a year of good health. QALY units are gained from the beneficial effect of treatments. These units are balanced against the cost of providing the treatment.

QALYs provide an outcomes measure that assigns values or 'utilities' for health states on a scale of 0 to 1, where perfect health is defined as 1 and death as 0. QALYs can be assessed in a number of different ways, of which the following are the most common.

- *Rating scales.* This uses a scale that marks as end-points the best and worst states of health.
- *Time trade-off.* This assesses how many years of less than perfect health people would trade for a smaller number of years of full health.

- *Standard gamble.* Here people choose between less than perfect health and a gamble that they may die immediately or have full health for the rest of their lives. The QALY value is determined from people's choices as the probabilities of death or full health are varied.

The QALY has some appeal in the debate as to where investment priorities lie.

- It is a measure that includes both the quality and quantity of life.
- It provides a means of comparing very different interventions.
- It is a measure of outcome rather than of input or process.

Cost-Value Analysis in Health Care, by Erik Nord, provides further details of the QALY and how it is calculated and used.[4]

However, the QALY is not without difficulties, including the following.

- It aims to assess the choices of society, where individuals in society may have very different preferences.

- It assumes that QALY units are uniform across all diagnostic groups. However, there is some evidence that the utility rating from people with one type of illness varies from that of individuals with another type of illness.

- Acute illnesses are perceived to have a greater impact on life than chronic illnesses where means of coping have been devised.

- It is not possible to estimate cost of treatment and care over multiple systems and long periods of a person's life.

- Any exercise to measure QALYs in a sufficiently large sample of the population has a high cost.

Disability-adjusted life years (DALYs)

The World Bank Development Report of 1990 introduced the concept of DALYs. The DALY is a summary indicator that describes the burden of disease for a population.

DALYs combine the loss from premature death (defined as the difference between the actual age of death and life expectancy at that age in a low-mortality population) with the loss of healthy life resulting from a disability. For a detailed explanation of the equation, see *The Disability-Adjusted Life Year (DALY): definition, measurement and potential use.*[5] In summary, calculation of the DALY requires population estimates by age and sex, death rates for each ICD9 code, and morbidity.

The DALY aims to determine the complete burden that a disease exacts. The greater the impact of the disease on the quality of life, and the longer that the effects of the disease last, then the greater the burden of that disease will be. For example, an acute illness from which there is swift recovery is less of a burden than a chronic one that leaves a continuing disability. And a disability that arises in childhood contributes more to the calculation of the DALY than one that arises in old age.

The DALY enables healthcare activity to be examined in relation to a particular service type, a specific set of diseases or risk factors, or a subset of the population.

The DALY is used to indicate where investments can be made that have the greatest impact on health gain. The intended use is in the setting of health priorities, identifying disadvantaged groups for targeting of interventions, and providing an output measure for the performance of interventions. In the UK this is most relevant with regard to the development and monitoring of Health Improvement Programmes (HImPs) at health authority level. It can suggest priorities for investment based on the cost-effectiveness of interventions, and it can be used to measure the extent to which health is improved. The health authority is also the level at which the Health Improvement Programmes are developed, and it is where the relevant data are most readily available.

A useful review of the principles, calculation and use of DALYs was undertaken by Dr Simon Crick for the NHS Eastern Region.[6]

The DALY is not without problems, including the availability of data and the effort involved in the calculation. This and other similar measures have underlying value questions that need to be examined. Perhaps the greatest benefit of these measures is to prompt debate on values, priorities and interventions and the inevitable rationing of publicly funded cash-limited service.

Financial control within organisations

Budgeting

Budgeting is the means of allocating revenue and controlling expenditure within an organisation. Many organisations use budgeting solely for this purpose. However, organisations that design budgets with only expenditure control in mind are missing a major opportunity to influence decision-making and performance-enhancing behaviour. Those responsible for designing budgets are also unlikely to understand the full effect that budget changes are having on behaviour, and as a result observe undesirable effects.

Figure 4.1 shows the many areas of an organisation that are affected by budgets.

Figure 4.1 Budgeting.

- *Planning*: The budget represents the financial plan of the organisation. Agreed objectives should go along with the financial allocation, with both being agreed during budget setting. These objectives will further the overall purpose of the organisation and provide the means for implementation of its priorities. Budgets therefore include activity as well as financial expectations.

- *Financial allocation*: The budget sets the distribution of financial resources.

- *Expenditure control*: Expenditure is monitored against the individual budgets. The budget report, which is normally calculated monthly, allows budget holders and financial controllers to monitor expenditure against expectations during the year. Any variations can be spotted and adjustments made to expenditure or to budget in year.

- *Decision timing*: Devolution of budgets, including the decisions on individual items of expenditure, means that decisions which affect the deployment of resources can be taken more rapidly than if each one must be referred to a central department within the organisation.

- *Driver for change:* Devolution of budgets is an effective means of increasing motivation. Smaller teams have responsibility for making financial decisions, and can use that power to achieve organisational as well as local objectives. For example, allocation of pathology budgets to clinical directorates through an internal process of re-charging the cost/price of pathology requests can change the motivation of both requesters and deliverers of the pathology service. The clinical directorate might be motivated to reduce its requesting activity in order to have money to commit to other clinical priorities. The pathology department is more likely to be motivated to reduce its unit costs.

- *Distribution of power:* Holding the responsibility for committing financial resources is a major source of power within an organisation. Through the allocation of budgets, power can be redistributed within an organisation, a factor that is likely to result in resistance to change in some quarters. Distribution can be used by senior management to 'reward' individuals or departments for achieving organisational objectives.

Approaches to budget setting

The main principle of budgeting is to put the responsibility for controlling the budget at the point where the decisions on commitment of resources are made. Where decisions on commitment are devolved, budget responsibility needs to be similarly devolved. Indeed, it is desirable to devolve commitment decisions to operational levels so that there is no undue delay in decision making. For example, when a ward manager authorises the deployment of an agency nurse, that manager is creating expenditure. If they also have responsibility for the budget covering agency nurses within their remit, then the priority of the clinical need as well as cost will be considered.

There are two main approaches to setting budgets within an organisation, namely incremental and zero-based budgets.

Incremental budgets

Most NHS budgets are based on the incremental approach. The new year budgets are based on the previous year's budget, with adjustments made to allow for increased and decreased activities. Most of the budget remains unchanged, as are the activities and outcomes that the budget is expected to achieve. Budget holders are not asked to justify what they do or how they do it. The main disadvantage of this approach is that it can perpetuate inefficiencies. The practice of reducing all budgets by a percentage each year in order to achieve efficiency gains has now largely stopped. While gross inefficiencies existed this method worked, but after a number of years without more fundamental review of processes, it began to hit core services.

Incremental budgets are simple and quick to construct and are suitable for stable environments.

Zero-based budgeting

Each year, budget holders are required to set a cost against each of the activities for which they are responsible, and also to identify the outcomes and benefits that are derived from that activity. Part of the budget-setting process then considers whether these activities should continue to be funded. This has the advantage that activities that are no longer of sufficient benefit to the organisation can be discontinued and the cost reinvested in higher priorities. The zero-based approach is little used, mainly because of the effort involved in its implementation and in the time taken to agree budgets. It is particularly suitable for environments that are undergoing change, where new activities are required and redundant ones are being dropped.

Whichever method is used, it is essential that sufficient flexibility exists in the process to encourage change in practices. Most healthcare environments are rapidly changing, and a budget set for a whole year is often no longer appropriate. There needs to be sufficient stability in the budget to allow forward planning of activities, combined with sufficient flexibility to allow response to changes within the year. There are several means by which this can be achieved:

- allowing budget holders to transfer funds across budget categories
- negotiation and agreement within the year to transfer funds between budget holders

- transfer of over-spending or under-spending from one financial year to the next.

Most healthcare organisations still operate functional budgets, allocating the budget to those departments where the expenditure occurs. There are alternative options designed to influence decisions on the commitment of resources and placing budgets where those commitments are made. An example of this is clinical budgeting.

Clinical budgeting

Clinical budgeting is the term applied to a management budgeting system that allocates to clinical departments or specialities (e.g. general surgery) the budgets for diagnostic and therapeutic support departments (e.g. pathology, pharmacy and physiotherapy).

It is the clinical departments or specialists that generate the activity and costs in the support departments by ordering tests, medications and therapies. By allocating the budgets to the clinical departments, they can have greater choice over how that money is spent in order to best meet the needs of their patients.

However, in the UK clinical budgeting is rare, unlike practices in other countries, such as Australia.

In the 1980s, CASPE undertook an experiment on clinical budgeting funded by the Department of Health.[7] The aim was to examine the way in which case mix might vary if consultants were given control of their own budgets. The results showed no evidence of case-mix changes, but there was evidence of reductions in resource use in those sites that had clinical budgeting. Planning agreements were made with clinical teams (PACTs), which covered the planned workload of the team, the resources required and planned achievements. During the year, information was provided to the clinical teams on activity and costs, comparing actual performance with that agreed in the PACT. This stimulated discussion of variations and resulted in changes to plans, expenditure or procedures.

The NHS Executive Resource Management Initiative (1986–92)[8] introduced the clinical directorate structure into UK hospitals with the aim of involving clinicians in management. This is still the predominant structure in the UK. With the introduction of clinical directorates, it was expected that clinicians would have greater control over decisions affecting resources, and that they would have control of more of the overall budget of the organisations as their management skills developed. The intention was that clinical budgeting should become the norm. This needed to be accompanied by an appropriate information system – the Case-mix Management System. Although all of the large hospitals in the UK procured such systems, few of them were properly implemented, and most have now disappeared.

Full clinical budgeting requires a method that derives the cost of individual events or interventions (e.g. a day stay, pathology test, operating procedure, etc.). The standard costing method is described in the section on 'Knowing the cost' (see page 92). This results in the full costs, including all overheads, being distributed to case-mix groups. Some implementations of clinical budgeting have tried to allocate this full cost to clinical groups. Although this is theoretically justifiable, in practice it tends to undermine the basic principle, since clinical groups have no control of the majority of that cost. It is therefore necessary to split the full cost and allocate elements of it to different budget holders. For example, clinicians make decisions on activity (the number and type of patients, tests and treatments). It is therefore appropriate that they are allocated budgets that cover costs affected by levels of activity (e.g. drugs budget, variable costs of diagnostic tests and staff directly employed in the clinical area). However, it is not reasonable for them to be allocated the overheads of, for example, the information department or finance department over which they have no control. This system requires that a standard cost is allocated to an activity, activities are linked to individual patients (and therefore clinical teams), and expenditure is monitored based on this standard cost.

The implementation of clinical budgeting in the UK has been limited. There were real short-term concerns that clinical behaviour could result in a large switch of resources, and that as a result the fixed costs could not be covered. Had the will been there, such concerns could easily have been overcome by a two-stage process of budget devolution, with variable costs being devolved first, and fixed costs later.

The following points were clear from the work undertaken.

1   Clinicians would influence their decisions on resource use if they were given a budget. That change relates to changes in inter-ventions (e.g. diagnostic tests, medications, appointments, thera-pies) rather than to changes in the mix of patients.

2   Authority for clinicians to reallocate savings proved to be a powerful influence on behaviour.
3   Clinicians needed financial support (e.g. a business manager within a clinical directorate) if they were to take on budgeting effectively.
4   There is a considerable amount of information required, including the following:
    • a measure of case mix (e.g. healthcare resource group (HRG) and diagnosis related group (DRG))
    • a costing/pricing methodology at the level of intervention
    • activity
    • expenditure by case-mix group and department.
5   Reconciling income with expenditure becomes difficult when income is fixed but expenditure is related to activity.

Many of the observed implementations of clinical budgeting have been over-ambitious and lost the basic principle of allocating monies where financial commitment decisions are made. As a result, many of them have turned into reporting exercises rather than influencing expenditure commitment decisions.

Budget reporting

Effective budgetary control is dependent on budget holders making commitments within their allocation. To do this, they need to be aware of expenditure against budget on a regular (normally monthly) basis. Shortcomings of the budget-reporting system are or were often the cause of uncontrolled expenditure.

Ideally, the budget-reporting system should be able to inform the budget holder of expenditure at any point in time. It should also indicate commitments made against the budget which have yet to be paid. In practice, there are often difficulties.

• Reports are often produced and distributed once a month, and then several weeks after the end of the previous month.
• Money may have been added to or removed from a budget without the knowledge or agreement of the budget holder.
• Items not under the control of the budget holder are set against the budget.
• Sufficient detail is not provided on individual transactions for the

budget holder to reconcile the budget report with their own knowledge.

- Most systems do not include commitments which are set against the budget possibly months later when payment is made, resulting in the more conscientious budget holder keeping a second system.

The budget statement, which is the budget holder's principal source of information for managing the budget, should show the following:

- expenditure against a number of budget categories (e.g. staffing, equipment, consumables, etc.)
- the amount of budget remaining
- the projected end-of-year out-turn on the budget.

Many hours have been wasted trying to use budget statements that appeared to be incorrect, only to find that certain committed items had not yet appeared on the statement, an item was miscoded against the budget when it should have gone elsewhere, or other events had occurred that were not notified. Those keen to maintain budget control normally resort to keeping their own personal record of commitments made. The addition of the following items would have saved much time:

- the amount committed against each category (available from orders)
- individual items of expenditure against each category (for checking and confirmation).

Budgets are often shown as 12 equal monthly amounts, although expenditure is rarely equal throughout the year. Consider the example where expenditure is lower in the early months covered by the budget, and higher in the later months. For example, an energy budget might show this pattern. With equal monthly budgets, a budget holder could be misled into thinking that they were under-spent on their budget, when in fact the reverse might be true.

Budget holders' individual knowledge combined with analysis of previous expenditure will reveal a pattern of expenditure throughout the year, and the monthly distribution of the budget can be decided accordingly. Where this is done, both the monthly picture and the projected end-of-year out-turn are likely to be closer to reality.

Budget flexibility

In a stable environment where the activities and expenditure are similar in one year to those in the previous year, it makes sense to set incremental budgets. This may apply to some departments. However, it is far more common for greater flexibility to be required to cater for in-year changes.

Business planning

The business-planning process, incorporating the production of business cases, is the main means by which organisations allocate capital.

An agreed format for a business case and the information that is required for investment decisions to be made is essential if proper consideration is to be given to investments. The business case also forms the basis for monitoring the investment and its implementation to ensure that:

- implementation is within an agreed time-scale
- estimated costs are not exceeded
- benefits are identified and achieved.

The detail needed in the business case and the process of authorisation will depend on the level of investment anticipated.

There are various models for developing business cases, but the principles are the same, and the format and content of all of them are similar. The business case sets out the following information.

- *Strategic case.* This describes the strategic objectives that the investment aims to achieve in relation to the overall purpose and aims of the organisation.
- *Option appraisal.* This is description of the various options for achieving the objectives, with details of the costs, benefits and risks of each option. The preferred option and the reasons for preference are discussed. Rarely is there a single option, and only occasionally is one option clearly better than the rest. A low-cost option may not achieve as many benefits, and a high-cost option may have a greater associated risk. The way in which the investment will be deployed is also considered. Will it be through procurement or internal development? Does it need external support or are sufficient skills and time available within the organisation for successful implementation?

- *Financial appraisal.* This describes the financial aspects of the preferred option in more detail, including costs, benefits and risks. It also describes how the project will be financed and, where financing is expected to come from benefits, how those benefits will be achieved to release cash. The affordability is assessed within guidelines agreed by the organisation. For example, where a project is required in order to meet legislation, this may be at a cost. Alternatively, where an investment improves the way in which certain activities are carried out, then it may be required to result in overall cash savings. It should also describe the impact that the investment will have on other parts of the organisation, in terms of both activity and money.

- *Management case.* This describes the management structures and processes that will be used to manage the project, including its planning, management and evaluation. A standard for UK public sector organisations is PRINCE II (Projects in a Controlled Environment).[9]

Considerable effort has gone into the standardisation of business cases for Private Finance Initiative projects and for information technology projects, because of the size, complexity and poor track-record of benefit realisation for these types of project.[10] A standard format for all business cases within a single organisation will help to assess their relative merits, and will also ensure that those submitting cases have thought about all of the issues involved.

As a result of capital investment, the distribution of activities and the cost of those activities will change. This may increase or decrease the costs of departments that are indirectly involved by the investment. Budgets may need to be changed as a result. The impact on all parts of the organisation needs to be considered in the business case and agreements on subsequent budget change need to be reached before the investment is made, otherwise the benefits outlined in the business case may not be achievable.

There are likely to be revenue consequences of capital investment – the ongoing costs resulting from the scheme. For example, if a new operating theatre is built as a capital scheme, it will have ongoing revenue requirements for staff, equipment, etc. If equipment is bought, it is likely to require regular maintenance. Provision needs to be made for these costs before approval is given for the go-ahead of a project. One of the consequences is the need to account for ongoing capital charges. The NHS is expected to make a 6% return on investment.

As well as the allocation of additional capital, the business-planning process should also consider disinvestment or reinvestment from activities that are no longer appropriate.

Key points

- Finance is perhaps the most powerful driver for change, much more so than 'balancing the books'. The means of allocation and expenditure have a major influence on behaviour.
- The principle of financial allocation in the NHS is to provide fair and equitable healthcare for the whole population.
- In a cash-limited service, financial allocation measures must consider what services have priority and how rationing is to be achieved.
- The design of the budget-setting and budget-management processes has a major influence on the expenditure behaviour of individuals and departments.
- Various measures aim to assess the value of healthcare to society and to set priorities accordingly.

References

1 *Health Authority Cash Limits Exposition Handbook*. www.doh.gov.uk/allocations

2 Department of Health (2000) *Departmental Report. The Government's expenditure plans*; www.doh.gov.uk/dohreport/report2000

3 Convisor R, Retondo M and Loveless M (1995) *Universal Health Coverage, Rationing and HIV Care: lessons from the Oregon Health Plan Medicaid Reform*. Self-published.

4 Nord E (1999) *Cost-Value Analysis in Health Care: make sense out of QALYs*. Cambridge University Press, Cambridge.

5 Homedes N (1995) *The Disability-Adjusted Life Year (DALY): definition, measurement and potential use*. Available at http://www.worldbank.org/html/extdr/hnp/hddflash/workp/wp_00068.html

6 Crick S (2000) *Scoping Paper: the burden of disease and the use of DALYs in planning healthcare services*. NHS Executive, Eastern Region, Cambridge.

7 Jones T and Prowle M (1987) *Health Service Finance: an introduction*. The Certified Accountants Educational Trust, London.

8 NHS Management Board (1986) *Resource Management Health Notice*. NHS Management Board, London.

9 Office of Government and Commerce (formerly CCTA) *PRINCE II (Projects in a Controlled Environment)*; www.ogc.gov.uk/prince

10 South West NHS Executive Regional Office (2000) *Five-Case Model*

for IT Investment. South West NHS Executive Regional Office, Bristol.

5 Managing quality and cost

Introduction

Managing quality and cost are considered together. Why?

> There is a balance to be struck between the process, level of activity and unit cost. This is particularly true of a publicly funded, cash-limited service.

Much of the information needed to manage quality and cost is the same.

The following discussion can be applied to any activity within the organisation, but is principally considered here in relation to the direct care and treatment of patients and the clinical support services. In this case:

- process = the events and interventions involved in the care/treatment
- activity = the number of patients treated
- cost = the cost of each individual patient (derived from the unit cost of each event or intervention in the process).

Healthcare services could always do more than the available resources allow. Technological developments make more treatments possible. These 'high-tech' treatments are often expensive. The theory on which the NHS was founded was that investment in healthcare would improve the health of the population and thus reduce the investment necessary in the longer term. However, this has never happened. Improved and new treatments lead to increased expectations among the population. Patients survive for longer with chronic conditions that require ongoing support, and more people survive to old age with its share of ongoing health needs. There will always be discussion about what is available to which people, but the care of individual patients, once admitted to the system, must always be based on the best available practice.

Quality and cost are not always in opposition. Evidence shows that high-quality care costs less than poor-quality care. 'Getting it right first time', having fewer avoidable complications and eliminating unnecessary interventions while providing better clinical outcomes and improving patient satisfaction all contribute to improved quality at lower cost.

Managing quality and cost principally involves understanding the cost of resources and how they are deployed to provide quality outcomes. Information for maximising quality and minimising cost is an essential element of running a cost-limited publicly funded service.[1]

Clinical governance

This section will consider the information that is required for clinical governance in so far as it is important to provision and use of resources within a healthcare organisation.

Clinical governance involves organisational accountability for the effective use of resources, clinical practice and performance, as well as health outcomes. It arises from the need to ensure patient safety. It is the principal means by which the quality of clinical care is assured within the UK NHS, and was introduced by the Blair Government in response to concern about adverse incidents. Additional evidence comes from a US survey which indicated that between 44 000 and 98 000 patients in American hospitals die from avoidable mistakes every year.[2] Investigations highlighted the need to increase clinical accountability and in particular the need for Chief Executives and directors to have clinical as well as financial responsibility for their organisations.

The detailed requirements for clinical governance were set by the Department of Health in 1997.[3]

A quality organisation will ensure that:

- quality improvement processes (e.g. clinical audit) are in place and integrated with the quality programme for the organisation as a whole
- leadership skills are developed at clinical team level
- evidence-based practice is in day-to-day use with the infrastructure to support it
- good practice, ideas and innovations (which have been evaluated) are systematically disseminated both within and outside the organisation

- clinical risk reduction programmes of a high standard are in place
- adverse events are detected and openly investigated, and the lessons learned are promptly applied
- lessons for clinical practice are systematically learned from complaints made by patients
- problems of poor clinical performance are recognised at an early stage and dealt with in order to prevent harm to patients
- all professional development programmes reflect the principles of clinical governance
- the quality of data collected in order to monitor clinical care is itself of a high standard.

This requires that information is readily available, including the following:

- evidence on which clinical care and treatment are based
- what constitutes best practice
- evidence that best practice is being used
- adverse incidents and complaints.

Information for Health,[4] published by the NHS Executive in 1998, provided a national information strategy which was placed in the context of Government policy and described information objectives and targets to provide the required information. These targets included the following:

1   1998–2000:
    - connecting all computerised GP practices to NHS*net*
    - offering *NHS Direct* services to the whole population.[5]
2   2000–2002:
    - 35% of all acute hospitals to have implemented Level 3 electronic patient records (EPRs) (*see* Appendix 3)
    - use of NHS*net* for appointment booking, referrals, radiology and laboratory requests/results in all parts of the country
    - community prescribing with electronic links to GPs and the Prescription Pricing Authority
    - telemedicine and telecare options considered routinely in all Health Improvement Programmes
    - a National electronic Library for Health accessible through local intranets in all NHS organisations.[6]

3   By 2005:
- full implementation at primary care level of first-generation person-based electronic health records
- all acute hospitals with Level 3 EPRs
- electronic transfer of patient records between GPs
- 24-hour emergency-care access to patient records.

By early 2001, the National electronic Library for Health (NeLH) was to provide a rich source of information, including the following.

1   Know-how:
- NICE (National Institute for Clinical Excellence) guidance
- National Service Frameworks (NSFs)
- NeLH Guidelines Database
- NICE referral practice leaflet.
2   Access to knowledge:
- *Clinical Evidence*
- Cochrane Library
- *Evidence Based on Call*
- NHS Economic Evaluation Database
- MEDLINE/PubMed
- Research Findings Register
- Health Technology Assessment (HTA) Publications
- Reviews of Effectiveness (DARE)
- *Effective Healthcare Bulletins*
- *Managing to Make a Difference.*

Details of progress and the most recent guidance can be found on the NHS Information Authority website.[7]

For a long time the quality of care was regarded as the responsibility of the clinical staff, while the cost of care was regarded as the responsibility of general managers. In the UK these responsibilities have been brought together with common accountability for corporate governance and clinical governance. There is evidence, mainly from the USA, that high-quality care is also cost-effective care.[8] It is no coincidence that commercial companies throughout the world have adopted quality programmes – quality affects the bottom line. Healthcare is no different in wanting to provide high quality, with increasing emphasis being placed not only on quality as defined by healthcare professionals, but also on the views of patients.

Cost-containment programmes tend to result in a decrease in quality of service, but the quality improvement programmes can result in cost containment.

There are a number of areas where poor quality increases costs:

- unnecessary interventions (e.g. diagnostic tests, medications)
- not 'getting it right first time' (e.g. the need for revision of hip replacements or unsuccessful keyhole surgery)
- avoidable complications (e.g. postoperative infections)
- imbalance of resources (e.g. lack of theatre time or access to diagnostic facilities, leading to cancelled appointments or increased length of stay)
- employee turnover and consequent training costs.

The patient-based information described above, linking process, outcomes and cost, allows quality and cost to be linked in the management process.

Prospective vs. retrospective information

When managing quality, the use of both prospective and retrospective information is important. As mentioned earlier, prospective information is used to 'get it right first time', whereas retrospective information is used to spot cases where this did not happen. Clinical trials are an example of the use of prospective information to assess the efficacy of a new medication or clinical process. The other major use of retrospective information is to identify patterns across groups of patients and across time. These patterns may suggest improvements that cannot be identified from a single individual.

Operational systems for direct clinical care and administration can also be utilised to support decisions that result in improved use of resources.

Example 5.1   Predicting future bed usage: 1 to 2 weeks ahead

The need for emergency beds can be predicted with some degree of accuracy. Past patterns give a baseline of usage on to which increased use due to adverse weather conditions and epidemics can be superimposed. The information for this is readily available from patient administration systems.

Elective bed use can also be predicted. Once a patient is given an admission date, their likely bed occupancy is known from a profile for their condition, and the necessary bed days can be booked. This can be refined by factoring in other characteristics where relevant (e.g. the age of the patient or their home circumstances).

Routinely using such information has an impact in a number of areas.

- Effort involved in cancellation when beds are not available and subsequent rescheduling can be avoided. For many patients, the hospital event itself is a trauma that is compounded when cancellations are made.
- Planned changes in bed numbers and associated staffing can be made. The introduction of flexible working practices makes this increasingly feasible.
- Improvements in quality and cost are the result.

Example 5.2   Health service waste under fire as funds increase

Poor hygiene in hospitals contributes to one in ten patients contracting an infection which costs the NHS in England £1 billion a year to treat, the Public Health Laboratory Service[9] said. Better infection control procedures, backed by additional resources, could yield significant savings.

In a separate report on financial management of the NHS, the Commons Public Accounts Committee[10] said hundreds of millions of pounds are lost to fraud and clinical negligence. An estimated £150 million is lost on prescription fraud, and the 15 000 cases of clinical negligence that are pending could cost another £2.8 billion.

Jeremy Laurance, Health Editor, *Independent*, 19 January 2000

It is not only administrative uses of information that can improve the quality and cost of patient care.

Example 5.3   Doctors' errors cost NHS £2 billion a year

One in ten people who are admitted to hospital will be damaged by medical errors which cost the health service £2 billion to put right, it was acknowledged yesterday as the Government unveiled ambitious proposals to transform the blame culture inside the NHS and learn from mistakes.

Every year around 850 000 patients admitted to hospitals suffer some sort of harm – usually of a minor nature but sometimes serious – according to a report published yesterday by Liam Donaldson, the Government's Chief Medical Officer. Preventable tragedies include the deaths of children wrongly given injections in their spine, and babies who were stillborn because the monitor that should have registered their distress was recording the mother's heartbeat and not that of the fetus.

Sarah Boseley and Geoffrey Gibbs, *The Guardian*, 14 June 2000

Most errors are not caused by a single person failing in a single act, but tend to be compounded systems errors. The aim is to detect a potential error and prevent it from happening. The errors described here will only be prevented by prospective means, getting the clinical and administrative processes right and making information an integral part of those processes.

The use of protocols and guidelines provides a means of standardising processes and identifying deviations from the standard process as they occur. Protocols detail the nature and timing of specific events anticipated for dealing with specific clinical conditions or procedures. Guidelines are of a more general nature, and are systematically developed statements that assist the clinician and patient in making decisions about the appropriate healthcare for a condition.

There are many sources of guidelines.

The National Institute for Clinical Excellence (NICE)[11] was set up as a Special Health Authority covering England and Wales in April 1999. Its role is to provide patients, professionals and the public with authoritative, robust and reliable guidance on current practice. In particular, it considers whether new treatments should be offered by the NHS. This guidance covers individual health technologies (e.g. medicines) and the clinical management of specific conditions.

NHS standards are described in National Service Frameworks, which are available from the National electronic Library for Health (NeLH).[12] They are implemented through clinical governance, underpinned by professional self-regulation and lifelong learning. Conformity with standards is monitored through the processes of the Commission for Health Improvement,[13] the National Performance Assessment Framework[14] and the National Survey of Patients.[15]

By early 2001, six National Service Frameworks had been published, which covered the following areas:

- mental health
- coronary heart disease
- older people
- cancer
- diabetes
- paediatric intensive care.

The Royal College of Nursing (RCN) provides guidelines on nursing practice.[16]

Guidelines and protocols are one means of prospectively managing quality and cost, but retrospective information also has an important part to play in:

- spotting errors after the event, to learn lessons from them and change processes as a result

- improving the care of individual patients in the future by analysing the experiences of patients in the past, and finding the lessons that can only be learned by investigating groups of similar patients.

Analysis of a statistically significant number of cases can point to poor performance of individuals or of the system as a whole, or it may identify 'the bad apple'. There is a need to compare like with like and therefore to group patients who are similar. There is also a need for a sufficiently large number of cases to ensure significance. This may require comparison over a large area or a long time period.

A simple illustration of the use of grouped information to assess the impact of a changing number of cases or to planning an increase or reduction in the levels of service is shown in Example 5.4 opposite.

Knowing the cost

Various methods of costing have been introduced over the years. Costing is an art, not a science – there is no such thing as the 'real cost'. The way in which costs are calculated will depend on the purpose to which they are to be put, and there is no single method of calculating cost that will meet all purposes. Many attempts at costing have fallen into disrepute at a later date, often because of the pursuit of the 'real cost', or because a cost determined for one purpose has been used for another for which it is not suited.

An example of this is the NHS Resource Management Initiative (1986–92). The purpose of costing in this context was to monitor the efficiency of healthcare provision and subsequently to set prices as part of the commissioning of healthcare. This initiative prepared the way for the method of costing used in 2000.

The Department of Health, in its *NHS Costing Manual* (latest revision November 2000),[17] sets out detailed and mandatory guidance for costing NHS services. The purpose is to ensure that costs are estimated consistently and can therefore be compared across the

Example 5.4 Implications of changing numbers of patients and patterns of care

A common requirement is to predict the implications for each individual department of an expected change in the numbers of patients, or in the ways in which they are treated. This may arise in any number of circumstances, but common ones would include:
- the introduction of a new service
- discontinuation of a service
- revised process as a result of clinical guidance
- changes in the numbers of cases as a result of service agreements with commissioners or a waiting-list initiative
- planning to increase or decrease capacity – new unit or hospital, or decommissioning.

In each case, the basic information process is the same, namely to determine:
- resource implications by department
- the cost of the change.

This example determines the resource implications of an expected increase in one particular patient group. In reality, it is likely that a number of different patient groups would be under consideration. The implications for each group would be determined separately and the results accumulated. The table below shows the activity implications of performing 50 cases of primary replacement of major joints.

	1 case	*50 cases*
Stay days	13	650
Major theatre hours	1.5	75
Medications (doses)	345	17 250
Simple biochemistry (tests)	7	350
Simple haematology (tests)	7	350
Simple microbiology (tests)	7	350
Simple histology (tests)	1	50
Nursing hours	29	1450
Healthcare assistant hours	28	1400
Other services (hours)	50	2500

The activity for one case will be that defined in the standard profile for a patient in this group. The standard profile can be obtained from an analysis of previous cases and from discussions with clinical staff. Where the organisation has a Case-mix Management System, this information will be readily available from that system.

This example shows each of the services as a broad grouping, but in reality more precise information would be available. For example, medications may be subdivided into different types. This gives a basis for costing the change and the basis for discussions with individual departments and their ability to manage the implications of them.

Be cautious when converting this activity to cost. In the section on calculating costs we discussed fixed and variable costs. Calculation of the standard cost of an event is dependent on the current level of activity. A small increase in, say, the requirement for pathology tests may be accommodated within existing resources, in which case only the variable element of the standard cost is incurred. A large increase, on the other hand, may require additional staff or equipment.

NHS. Revisions to the costing method were made following the abolition of the internal market, and an emphasis was placed on benchmarking costs between organisations. This has achieved widespread use of a consistent method, but has largely lost the use of costs for managing efficiency within an individual organisation.

The costing of all services provided by NHS organisations is governed by the following principles. Costs should be:

- calculated on a full absorption basis to identify the full cost of services delivered
- allocated and apportioned accurately by maximising direct charging or, where this is not possible, using standard methods of apportionment
- matched to the services which generate them in order to avoid cross-subsidisation.

It is a top-down costing method, of which there are three key elements:

1 a high-level control total based on actual costs by services identifying direct, indirect and overhead costs in line with the national minimum standards
2 a resource profile analysis of key conditions that represent at least 75% of the high-level control total, using available financial and information systems with specific reference to the clinician's knowledge of the conditions that they treat, the frequency with which they are performed, and the resources that are used to perform them
3 a continuous reconciliation process at all stages of the costing process, to ensure that all costs are recovered.

While the second element above stipulates the use of clinician knowledge to define the conditions, frequency and resources used, all service providers will have most of this information from routine data collection. It will be available from Patient Administration Systems. All hospitals that implemented Case-mix Management Systems would also have easy access to conditions and the resources used to treat them. However, these systems have largely fallen into disuse.

The involvement of clinicians is essential, not necessarily for the provision of basic data, but for understanding any local differences and how to interpret the information. It is clinicians who decide which patients are treated and how they are treated, and who order individual interventions. Apart from general overheads, it is therefore the clinicians who generate the cost. Their understanding and support are therefore essential if clinical behaviour is to change to alter those costs.

The costs that are derived are suitable for comparison between different organisations, for identifying inefficiencies, and for commissioning services. They are not suitable for budgeting within an organisation.

Table 5.1 summarises the standard top-down costing method described in the *NHS Costing Manual*. Readers who require further details of the method should refer to the manual.

Table 5.1 National standard costing process

Level/step	Description
Level 1	Establish full cost of providing services (control total)
Level 1, step 1	General ledger reconciliation
Level 2	Production of high-level control totals
Level 2, step 1	Attribute costs to specialties/services/programmes (directly or apportioned)
Level 2, step 2	Identify costing pools (fixed, semi-fixed and variable)
Level 2, step 3	Identify key cost drivers – establish a cost driver for each costing pool
Level 3	Establish control totals at point of delivery
Level 3, step 1	Disaggregate high-level control totals – allocate high-level control totals to points of delivery (e.g. outpatients, inpatients)
Level 3, step 2	Identify relevant activity data – allocate to points of delivery

All NHS providers are required to cost their services to at least level 3. Many now go on to level 4 for many services

Level 4	Identification and costing of resource profiles/client groups
Level 4, step 1	Identify Healthcare Resource Groups (HRGs) (inpatients and day patients)
Level 4, step 2	Trimming and truncation – cases with abnormally long length of stay
Level 4, step 3	Set up resource profiles (costed HRGs)
Level 4, step 4	Establish costed HRGs (average HRG costs) by relating the costs to the activity for each condition/procedure
Level 4, step 5	Costing the residue. The residue consists of the above average cost relating to excess bed days and low-cost and low-volume HRGs not specifically costed

Definitions used in costing include the following.

- *Direct costs*: Those costs that can be directly attributed to a cost centre. For example, the drugs prescribed by a particular doctor or to a particular patient can be directly attributed to that specialty or patient.

- *Indirect costs*: Those costs that cannot be directly attributed to a cost centre. For example, the cleaning of a ward block is unlikely to be directly attributable to a particular specialty or patient, but can be attributed to or shared between a number of them.
- *Overheads*: The costs that contribute to the general operation of the services (e.g. central management costs, finance department, information department).
- *Fixed costs*: These do not vary with changes in activity (e.g. rent and rates).
- *Semi-fixed (or step) costs*: These are fixed up to a certain level of activity and then increase in a step. For example, if inpatient activity decreases, less nursing time is required, but the number of nurses is unlikely to decrease unless a whole ward is closed.
- *Variable costs*: These vary directly with the level of activity.
- *Cost pool*: This brings together costs into identifiable groups (e.g. wards) and allows them to be allocated or apportioned to relevant services.
- *Cost drivers*: These are factors that determine the cost (*see* Table 5.2).

Table 5.2 Examples of cost drivers

Driver	Cost pool
Length of stay	Time-based ward costs (e.g. catering)
Admission	Condition-based ward costs (e.g. medical records)

Effective cost management aims to make a greater proportion of the overall costs variable and direct. This underlies much of the theory of management budgeting, private finance initiatives (PFI) and service level agreements.

The result of this top-down costing is to obtain an average cost for specific conditions or procedures through a process of directly allocating or apportioning the full costs of providing the service.

Comparing the costs both within an organisation and between

organisations highlights differences – where a procedure or service is more or less costly than the same or a similar service.

- What should the cost be for that service or procedure?
- How does cost relate to outcome?
- What is the variation in cost between different service users for the same service or the same procedure? Is this variation appropriate?
- If a high cost is suggesting wasted resources, where is the waste? Is it in a general overhead, a clinical support service or a direct service?
- Is the variation due to variation in volume, unit cost of service element or clinical process?

Any attempt to answer some of these questions requires not only the top-down costing process, but also a bottom-up costing process.

The bottom-up costing process requires that standard or average costs are calculated using the top-down process (described previously) down to the level of an individual event. The definition of 'event' will vary from one organisation to another and from one department to another depending on the level of sensitivity of costing required and the availability of information. It is anticipated that organisations will start with fairly broad definitions of an event (e.g. haematology test) and refine these as better information becomes available (e.g. full blood count). Having derived the cost for each event, patient costs are then derived using a bottom-up approach, summing the cost of all events for individual patients. Since not all patient events are likely to be captured individually on the patient record, some of the costs will be apportioned (e.g. to a patient episode, bed day or attendance). Costs such as catering and domestic costs are more appropriately apportioned to bed day, whereas physiotherapy cost may be more appropriately apportioned to episode.

As more organisations introduce electronic patient records, costing using this process becomes easier and less time-consuming.

Having derived a cost for each individual patient based on the standard/average cost of each event, it is possible to start to answer some of the questions posed above and to see how costs might be reduced or where costs should be increased in order to improve outcomes or achieve efficiency improvements elsewhere.

Reference costs

What are reference costs?

Through the National Schedule of Reference Costs,[18] unit cost information is shared across the NHS. The aim is to facilitate meaningful discussions between health authorities, primary care groups and NHS trusts on variations in the cost of services. It is planned that reference costs should be available across all secondary and specialist services in the UK by 2004.

The National Schedule of Reference Costs is only of value if the cost information is accurate, produced on a consistent basis, and comprehensive. Costing at the level of healthcare resource groups (HRGs), which is level 4 of the National Standard Costing Process, is required to ensure that organisations will be comparing like with like. The aim is to publish costs in categories that reflect the clinical need of patients and therefore the resources used for their treatment. For example, it would be unrealistic to expect a primary hip replacement to have a similar cost to a hernia repair. However, it would be reasonable to expect a hip replacement in one hospital to have a similar cost to a hip replacement in another hospital.

The reference costs allow organisations to identify how their costs compare with similar costs elsewhere, and to seek explanations for any variation. This allows organisations to detect areas of inefficiency and make improvements. It also allows commissioners of healthcare to see which organisations are operating more effectively than others.

There are good reasons why some cost variation exists, and cost should only be one of the factors that are taken into consideration when services are being planned and agreements are being nego-tiated. However, when there can be a difference of sixfold or more in the cost of apparently similar patients, with similar clinical needs, amongst organisations, it is reasonable that questions should be asked. Table 5.3 is an extract from the published tables for the year 2000. It shows the difference in cost of primary hip replacement in four trusts. This information is publicly available for named trusts, and it allows every hospital in the UK to see how its costs compare with the others.

Table 5.3 Reference costs for primary hip replacement (HRG H02: primary hip replacement)

	Elective inpatient FCEs*	Elective inpatient bed days	HRG mean cost (£)
Acute NHS Trust A	376	4286	4234
Acute NHS Trust B	292	2913	3617
Acute NHS Trust C	239	3185	2912
Acute NHS Trust D	238	2092	2396

*Finished consultant episodes.

Figure 5.1 shows the cost of primary hip replacement for all 183 organisations in the investigation.

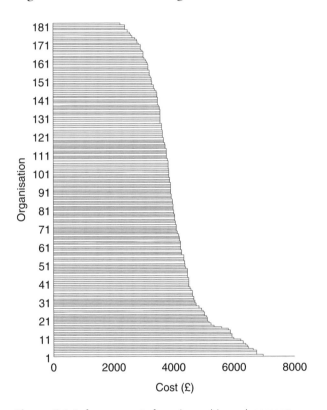

Figure 5.1 Reference costs for primary hip replacement.

The costs of each individual hospital are published for only a few HRGs, but this does not prevent a hospital knowing its own cost for any HRG, comparing itself with the national reference cost for the following:

- elective inpatients – people admitted to hospital from waiting-lists, and whose care requires staying in hospital for longer than a day
- non-elective inpatients – usually people admitted for urgent or emergency treatment
- day cases – people treated without an overnight stay
- critical care – the number of occupied bed days in intensive-care and high-dependency units
- outpatients
- radiotherapy
- Accident and Emergency
- community services.

Tables 5.4 and 5.5 show extracts from the HRG cost tables for elective patients and critical care services.

Limitations and the future

Although a great deal of use can be made of the published information on reference costs, there are limitations.

Most measures of case mix apply to inpatients, to outpatients or to patients in other specific care settings. As such, any costs calculated by case mix alone only cover part of the care or treatment for a particular condition. Patients have packages of care that include care and treatment across a range of care settings. For example, in a hospital a patient might have one or more outpatient appointments, followed by inpatient treatment, possibly involving critical care, and then a further one or more outpatient sessions. Information for the entire patient journey is not readily available at present, but will increasingly become so as electronic patient records (EPRs) become commonplace, as EPRs link all events and resources used in the treatment of the patient.

Example 5.5 shows how the limitation of comparing activity and cost in a single care setting can distort the view of developing clinical processes.

Table 5.4 Elective inpatients

HRG code	HRG label	Number of FCEs	Average cost (£)	Range for 50% of NHS trusts		Range for all NHS trusts		Number of bed days	Average length of stay (days)
				Minimum cost (£)	Maximum cost (£)	Minimum cost (£)	Maximum cost (£)		
A01	Intracranial procedures except trauma – Category 1	740	1509	775	1864	53	4479	2406	3
A02	Intracranial procedures except trauma – Category 2	2668	2599	847	2615	176	7896	14 714	6
A03	Intracranial procedures except trauma – Category 3	2060	3767	1079	3791	215	8605	17 138	8
A04	Intracranial procedures except trauma – Category 4	2191	5512	1282	6290	344	16 571	2,526	9
A05	Intracranial procedures for trauma with complications	143	4854	1849	5617	340	15 999	1663	12

Table 5.5 Critical care

Service type	Number of bed days	Average cost (£)	Range for 50% of NHS trusts		Range for all NHS trusts	
			Minimum cost (£)	Maximum cost (£)	Minimum cost (£)	Maximum cost (£)
Intensive-therapy unit/intensive-care unit	448 930	1103	961	1315	303	3203
Burns intensive-care unit	8800	1094	825	1287	535	1395
Neurosurgical intensive-care unit	16 617	768	528	1058	290	1253
Coronary-care unit	271 493	388	309	466	89	1312
High-dependency unit (if discrete ward/bed)	105 971	459	389	642	166	1470
Paediatric intensive-care unit	57 144	1196	981	1395	484	2076
Neonatal intensive-care unit – level 1	138 369	724	623	866	194	1344
Neonatal intensive-care unit – level 2	101 646	442	388	549	176	1149
Special-care baby unit	547 992	264	199	323	95	2466

Example 5.5 Varicose veins

Hospitals in a benchmarking club compared their relative proportion of varicose veins cases who were treated as day patients. At the time, varicose veins cases were expected to be treated either as inpatients or, increasingly, as day patients (which was preferred by patients and cost less than the inpatient treatment). The participants were surprised to find that the hospital which was normally at the forefront of developing day-case treatment had a relatively low proportion of day cases compared with their proportion of inpatients. On further investigation it was found that the hospital was now pioneering outpatient treatment for these patients, who were therefore not included in the figures. The outcomes for outpatient treatment were just as good, patients preferred the shorter visit to the hospital, and the costs were even lower than for day cases.

The reference costs give the average costs for all patients within a single HRG or service area within an organisation. Further analysis of variation within an HRG is needed to identify or at least narrow down the cause of that variation between hospitals. Is it due to a small number of exceptional cases or are the majority of cases costing more? The actions that would be taken in these two situations are very different. In the first, the exceptional cases would be identified and investigated. In the second situation, the overall process of care would be reviewed.

Managing efficiency and managing cost

Efficient: achieving objective at minimum cost.
Cost: expenditure in achieving an objective.

Efficiency and cost are different but related concepts that are often confusingly used interchangeably. For many years, UK healthcare providers have been charged with meeting 'efficiency improvement targets' – that is, year-on-year reductions in the cost of providing the same level of healthcare. These are really 'cost reduction targets' that penalise those organisations which are the most efficient.

Understanding the cost is an essential starting point for understanding the efficiency. In a National Audit Office report on hip replacements,[19] the following was one of the main findings on hip replacements:

A primary total hip replacement costs between £384 and £7784, depending in part on the complexity of the procedure. The average cost is £3755. Around one-third of trusts have reviewed their costs, but around one-third had difficulty in providing us with complete and accurate cost data. Without the basic information it is hard to see how these trusts can control costs effectively.

The standard NHS costing method gives an average cost using a defined top-down apportionment of the full costs of the organisation. In the National Schedule of Reference Costs, the NHS Executive Director of Finance indicates that the purpose of this is to 'facilitate meaningful discussions between health authorities, primary care groups and NHS trusts on variations in the cost of services.' But how does this help an organisation to manage its own costs or efficiency?

We might assume that if an organisation is at the higher end of the cost scale, this may indicate a low level of efficiency and room for a reduction in certain costs. It raises questions but does not provide definitive answers. There may be reasons why costs are high (e.g. if the organisation deals with relatively more complex cases in a specific high-cost area than the other organisations). Clearly it points to areas for investigation. However, if costs are average or even at the lower end of the spectrum, what then?

Before action can be taken to improve efficiency or reduce costs, further information is needed.

1   Which particular costs are high?
    - Is it activity in a particular patient group or speciality? Increasingly the standard costs can point in a particular direction.
    - Is it the direct costs of providing the service that are high? Or is it general overheads such as non-clinical support services (finance, administration, etc.)? Comparing the higher-level costs will give an indication of this.
2   What is the variability of costs for different patients? This requires a bottom-up costing method based on the standard cost of the different elements that make up the patient profile (e.g. visit, medication or diagnostic test), similar to that proposed by the Resource Management Initiative and provided by a Case-mix Management System.[20]
3   Are the desired health or healthcare outcomes being achieved at the minimum cost?

Most healthcare providers are a long way from being able to answer the latter two questions, and therefore from beginning to understand efficiency, let alone manage it.

In the absence of such information, organisations tend to use a process of cost reduction as a proxy, often with the result of a reduction in quality of care.

For many years healthcare providers have been subject to the need to meet annual efficiency improvement targets. These are expressed as a percentage of overall turnover for the whole organisation. When such measures started, it was common practice for the organisation to translate these overall targets into a reduction in every budget by the same percentage. Where gross inefficiency existed, it was relatively easy for a department to make savings without affecting the quality of the service provided. However, many organisations continued this practice even after such 'wastage' had been eliminated. Such practice could then only impact on the quality of care. Example 5.6 shows that there are still financial improvements to be gained from improving performance and eliminating waste.

Example 5.6 The cost of poor hygiene

In a Public Health Laboratory Service Report (2000) it was estimated that poor hygiene in hospitals contributes to one in ten patients contracting infections, and that this costs the NHS in England £1 billion a year in treatment costs. They further suggested that better infection control procedures, backed by additional resources, could yield significant savings.

It has been suggested that a number of factors contributed to reduced cleanliness of hospitals, including cost reductions on cleaning services and basic hygiene procedures of nurses.

The Socio-Economic Burden of Hospital-Acquired Infection,
Public Health Laboratory Service, 2000

Individual budget holders would look for areas where it was easiest to cut costs. This was often in staffing and training – the two areas most likely to have an adverse impact on quality of care. Reductions in staffing were often encouraged across the organisation through the imposition of recruitment freezes that had a totally arbitrary effect on where cuts were made – where a member of staff left for whatever reason.

More enlightened organisations recognised two things.

1   Efficiency was improved by considering the processes whereby outcomes were achieved and the optimising those processes.

Taking a whole-systems approach requires the investigation of processes that cross internal (if not external) organisational boundaries.

For example, it is likely to be more efficient to reduce the number of days that a patient stays in hospital and their risk of readmission, rather than focusing on the cost of an inpatient day and trying to reduce that.

2   Investment in one area is often required in order to achieve efficiency improvements elsewhere in the organisation. One holder's budget goes up to allow another's to be reduced.

For example, improvements in anaesthetic drugs mean that the patient recovery rates are improved, the risk of complications is reduced and the length of stay in hospital is reduced. However, these drugs are expensive. An increase in anaesthetic budget is required in order to reduce patient stay and reduce other budgets (e.g. wards). However, an increase in the anaesthetic budget without decreases elsewhere will only increase overall costs.

It should be immediately recognised that either of these courses of action requires greater and more difficult management intervention than cutting 2% off everyone's budget.

It is now recognised that efficiency and quality should go hand in hand. The Department of Health has outlined five ways in which more efficient and effective use of resources will be secured.[21]

1   Clinical and financial responsibility will be aligned. Primary care groups will be able to take devolved responsibility for a single unified budget covering most aspects of care, so that they can obtain the best fit between resources and need.

2   Management costs will be capped in health authorities and primary care groups, and the Government will continue to bear down on NHS trust costs. Transaction costs will be cut.

3   There will be a national schedule of reference costs itemising what individual treatments cost across the NHS, and NHS trusts will publish and benchmark their costs on the same basis.

4   There will be clear incentives for health authorities, NHS trusts and primary care groups to improve their performance and efficiency. For example, health authorities which perform well will be eligible for extra, non-recurrent cash. NHS trusts and primary care groups will be able to use savings from longer-term agreements to improve services for patients.

5 There will be clear sanctions if performance and efficiency are not up to standard. Health authorities will be able to withdraw freedoms from primary care groups. The NHS Executive will be able to intervene directly to rectify poor performance in any part of the NHS.

The National Performance Framework brings these developments together and aims to hold the NHS to account. It replaces the Purchaser Efficiency Index and concentrates on six areas, namely patient/carer experience, fair access to services, health outcomes of care, effective delivery of appropriate healthcare, efficiency and improvement in health.

The framework recognises that efficiency involves much more than reducing cost. However, the measures described focus on cost and comparing costs of different organisations. This can provide an indicator of the level of efficiency as well as some idea of where to look for improvements, although it does not suggest how they might be achieved.

There are a number of strategic approaches to improvement.

- *Statistical process control.* Understand the causes of variability of clinical processes and eliminate unwanted causes of that variability.[22]

- *Process analysis and development (business process re-engineering and other methods).* Review and optimise processes for anything from a protocol for clinical care, to discharging a patient, to providing supplies for a ward.

- *Management budgeting.* Adopt the well-accepted principle that the person who decides on the commitment of a resource should have the budget for that resource. For example, fixed costs of pathology (those incurred irrespective of the amount of work undertaken) would be allocated to the pathology budget and variable costs (incurred when a test is performed) would be allocated to the requesting department or speciality.

Case-mix groups

It will have become obvious from earlier sections that the concept of 'case mix' is important in many different aspects of management of resources. The model used is based on the concept of individual patients who can be placed in groups (case-mix groups) which are defined by their clinical characteristics. All patients within a single group will use similar packages of services. The aim is to describe the services provided by any provider organisation (e.g. hospital, community or GP practice), in a limited number of such groups (e.g. 75% of cases described by approximately 300 groups).

Background to case-mix groups

Experience in the USA

The diagnostic-related group (DRG) is an international standard for the classification of case mix. DRGs developed from the work of Robert B Fetter and his team in the 1960s, who were looking for a way to cost the output of a hospital.[23] These developments continued during the 1970s.

The original intention of the case-mix grouping was to provide a tool for the clinical and administrative management of hospitals, and to help to maintain the quality of care while minimising the cost of care. The business of a hospital is patient care, and therefore the focus must be on the patient. A classification was needed that met the following objectives.

- There should be medically meaningful classes of patients from homogeneous diagnostic categories. Clinicians should be able to identify a particular patient management process for patient classes.
- The classes should be defined using readily available data from hospital abstracts.
- There must be a manageable number of classes.
- The classes should contain patients with similar expected measures of output.

The expectation was that if these guidelines were used, patients within a class would use similar hospital resources, and that the classes would make sense to clinicians. DRGs resulted from work undertaken by Fetter and the Yale Research Group in conjunction with the Federal Government's Social Security Administration and the State of New Jersey's Department of Health. This work resulted in the creation of 383 groups, which become known as DRGs. These were used to construct a hospital payment system for the state of New Jersey, which was the first large-scale attempt in the USA to pay for hospital care prospectively on the basis of the hospital's case mix.

Patients are allocated a DRG on the basis of their principal diagnosis, operative procedure and, for some categories, age and presence of complications. Figure 5.2 shows how patients within the major diagnostic category (MDC) of diseases of the eye, based on their principal diagnosis, are allocated a DRG. DRGs continued to be developed, with various refinements being incorporated into different versions.

The fact that there is now knowledge and use of DRGs world-wide is testament to the years of work undertaken by Professor Fetter and his team, their commitment to open standards, and their willing distribution of definitions and grouping methodology.

Measures of case mix

There is a variety of measures of case mix other than DRGs (e.g. severity indices and disease staging for cancer).

Initial work in the USA and the UK focused on the development of groups to describe the work of acute hospitals. This was followed by classifications for outpatients, Accident and Emergency patients, mental health and care in the community.

Case mix in the UK

The concept of patient-based management information systems, and Case-mix Management Systems in particular, was given a major boost as part of the Resource Management Initiative that was launched in 1986. The programme was principally part of the organisational development of acute hospitals, encouraging the devolution of management – 'doctors in management'. An essential element of the programme was to ensure that this organisational development was underpinned by a patient-based information system.

The objectives of the initiative were formally set out in HN(86)34.[24] The principal objective was *to introduce a new approach to resource management and to demonstrate whether or not this resulted in measurable improvements in patient care.*

The subsidiary objectives were as follows:

- to identify areas of waste and inefficiency
- to benefit from clinical group discussion and review
- to highlight areas which could most benefit from more resources
- to identify and expose healthcare consequences of given financial policies and constraints

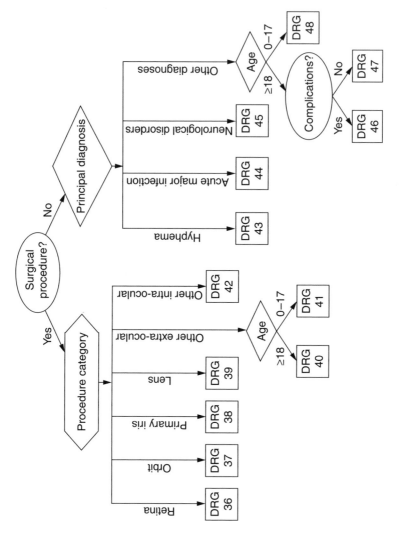

Figure 5.2 Deriving DRGs for diseases of the eye.[23]

- to understand the comparative costs of future healthcare options and hold informed debates about such options.

As in the USA earlier, it was recognised that a measure of case mix was essential to the achievement of these objectives. There had already been investigations into DRGs and their use, and this was the obvious classification to adopt. Two key pieces of research were carried out.

- Dr Hugh Sanderson at the London School of Hygiene's Department of Community Medicine conducted an evaluation of DRGs on a national sample of inpatient episodes.[25] This study identified potential use in service planning and monitoring.
- CASPE undertook experimentation with clinical budgeting to examine the way in which case mix might vary if consultants were given control over their own budgets. The results showed some evidence of reductions in resource use compared with control sites for the same case type.[26]

However, there were practical and political obstacles to the use of DRGs in the Resource Management Initiative.

- The basic classification systems for diagnosis and operative procedures were different in the USA and the UK.
- For some groups, resource use was highly variable.
- There were differences in clinical practice between the USA and the UK.
- The leading clinicians in the programme considered that acceptance of DRGs would mean acceptance of prospective payments at a future date.

Further work in the UK focused on the development of healthcare resource groups (HRGs) by the National Casemix Office, which was established in 1989 under the leadership of Dr Hugh Sanderson.[27] A priority for HRG development was the involvement and commitment of clinicians. The work of the National Casemix Office was subsequently incorporated into the NHS Information Authority.[28]

The Casemix Office developments have led to a series of linked classifications, providing a framework for describing local healthcare needs and comparint these with their provision. That framework is based on *the right people, having the right treatments, in the right place, with the right funding and coming to the right conclusion.*

The right people

Health benefit groups (HBGs) are groups of people with similar health conditions (as a proxy for similar need) who are expected to have similar outcomes when they receive a similar programme of care. HBGs provide an information base for developing services to meet local need.

The right treatments

Healthcare resource groups (HRGs) describe the mix of treatments undertaken and the resources required to provide them. They are used by healthcare providers to compare and monitor the care and treatment that they provide in terms of activity, resources and cost. They are used as the basis for the national standard costing system and national reference costs.

In the right place

Case-mix information, together with information about the local population (e.g. age, sex, income, etc.), is used to assess local need for healthcare, and can support debate on areas for investment.

With the right funding

Since case mix can help to identify local healthcare needs and then determine the resources needed to meet those needs, it could be used to inform funding allocations to local areas.

Coming to the right conclusion

This requires an understanding of the outcomes of the care or treatment that patients receive, and not just the inputs or resources that are used to care for or treat them. Although further developments are needed in this area, case mix is an important element. Given that case mix describes clinically meaningful groups of patients who consume similar resources, then the establishment and linking of outcome measures would provide the final link in the chain.

Clinical outcomes

In order to be able to monitor the whole of the healthcare process, the final piece of the information jigsaw that needs to be completed is a measure of outcome. There have been exercises to define outcomes, but a standard measure of outcome is still some way off.

The UK Clearing House on Health Outcomes, based at the Nuffield Institute at Leeds University, was established in 1992, funded by the NHS Management Executive, the Scottish Home and Health Department, the Welsh Office and the Northern Ireland Department of Health and Social Services.[29] It was set up to provide information and advice to the UK NHS on outcome measures and outcome measurement. It provides publications, information sheets and databases.

Scotland has taken a lead in the development of clinical outcome indicators. A range of indicators has been developed and published over the past 10 years.[30] The limits have now probably been reached with regard to what can be developed on the basis of currently available routine hospital discharge data. Further progress will be dependent on the collection and analysis of more sensitive data related to specific conditions.

The indicators that were developed from 1993 to 2000 are listed in Appendix 2. The indicators vary widely and include the following:

- true outcome indicators (e.g. 30-day survival after admission for heart attack)
- indicators of the process (e.g. caesarean section rates)
- population indicators (e.g. teenage pregnancy rates)
- specific clinical indicators (e.g. readmission after specific operations).

The indicators are standardised for whatever aspects of case mix are appropriate and are derived from readily available information. They can be used to identify the variation in outcome between different healthcare providers as an indicator of quality. Only some of the factors that contribute to the variation can be standardised (e.g. age, sex and deprivation). Some groups can be standardised for severity or stage of disease. However, as with any indicator, wide and consistent variation should raise questions about quality of care that require further investigation.

In their report on clinical outcome indicators[31] the Scottish Executive highlighted their use as shown in Box 5.1.

Box 5.1 Clinical outcome indicators

Legitimate use of such outcome indicators:
- provides useful clues and limited evidence relating to quality of care or performance
- focuses attention on variations in outcome which might have remained unsuspected, and which may warrant further investigation
- fulfils a 'backstop' monitoring role to highlight potential poor performance
- illustrates past performance that may provide an insight into current practice
- represents only one component of a comprehensive and concerted effort to provide a high standard of clinical care in the NHS.

Outcome indicators do not:
- include the patient's view about the outcome
- provide definitive proof of performance or quality of care
- constitute a 'league-table' of performance
- justify precipitate action in the absence of corroborative evidence.

The Scottish experience was that publication of the indicators led in some cases to formal reviews or undertaking of local audits, and resulted in service changes. Most commonly it was found that indicators reinforced a pre-existing suspicion that something needed to be done.

In England, the focus for outcomes information and research is the National Centre for Health Outcomes Development (NCHOD). This is based jointly at the Institute of Health Sciences at the University of Oxford, London School of Hygiene and Tropical Medicine and the University of London. The indicators that have been developed are available on the Clinical and Health Outcomes Knowledge Base,[32] which is available to the NHS via NHSnet.

There are considerable challenges to be addressed in the development of outcome measures.[33] They include the following.

- How is outcome defined? As a result, a change in state, or a benefit?

- Outcomes may be measured in different ways (e.g. in terms of impact on quality of life, function, or clinical signs and symptoms).

- Whose perspective should be taken? Should it be that of the patient, doctor, carer or policy maker?

Although outcomes measurement requires much further development, there are many measures, both direct and proxy, that are currently available.

Identifying variations in resource use

The process of healthcare can be described as patients demanding services which consume resources and result in outcomes. Patients have conditions (problems, symptoms or diagnoses) and a prognosis. Healthcare processes as defined in protocols are packages of resources use (consultations, investigations or treatments) which combine in episodes of care.[34]

This gives us the building blocks for our model. If the information is to be of use to clinical and general management, it must address the following:

- the service users and the reason for their use
- the resources consumed and the cost of those resources
- the quality of service received by each patient – service process, its outcome and the user's satisfaction.

In order to link clinical and general management processes and ensure that the resulting information is able to support a wide range of processes, the relationship between each of these factors needs to be investigated. This is achieved through a model based on the main focus of the service, namely the patient.

It is recognised that each patient is an individual, and that the treatment or care which they receive will be tailored to their individual requirements. However, in order to manage and plan for the future, it is necessary to identify similarities between patients and to group them. For each case-mix group, the expected package of services can be described. At an operational clinical level this package is described in detail in a *protocol*. For management purposes the protocol can be summarised in a *profile*. The profile may include the expected outcome for a patient within the group.

When actual patient activity is compared with the relevant profile, it gives rise to variations from that which was expected. There may be more or fewer patients in a particular group than expected (volume variation), they may have had more or fewer events than expected (process variation), or the proportions of patients across the groups may vary (case-mix variation). Each of these variations can be described in terms of the service measure itself (e.g. test) or expressed as a cost (£). This may be viewed for the hospital as a whole or disaggregated to give a view for the various organisational entities (e.g. programme, department or service).

115

Using case mix to manage resources

Each of these elements (case-mix groups, expected use of resources (profiles), actual use of resources, variation and outcomes) can be combined in an overall process for the management of resources as demonstrated in Figure 5.3.

Figure 5.3 shows:

- how the resources (1) used in the provision of service (2)
- resulting in outcomes for the patient (3)
- can be compared with expectations (4)
- which identify variations and lead to clinical or management action to modify the process, the resources or the expectations.

In addition, it shows:

- how monitoring the external environment (5)
- results in a check as to whether the expectations are still valid (6).

Setting up a 'double-loop' formal process such as this is important for any organisation that operates within a complex and changing environment. There are many examples where practices that were acceptable in the past are no longer acceptable because of changing technologies or societal views. Expectations as expressed in clinical protocols and procedures need to be modified as new evidence, medications, procedures or techniques become available. They also need to be developed as political and public expectations of the service change.

The activity information that is needed for such analysis is readily available in GP patient record systems, patient-based community systems and in patient administration systems. As organisations move towards electronic patient records linking a greater number of events (e.g. diagnostic tests and medications) to individual patients within and across organisations, this information will become increasingly useful as a means of managing quality and cost.

Once this information is available, it can be used in a variety of clinical and general management processes.

Audit

Topic audit

Individual patient records are selected for any group of patients or topic (e.g. patients having a particular diagnosis or those receiving a

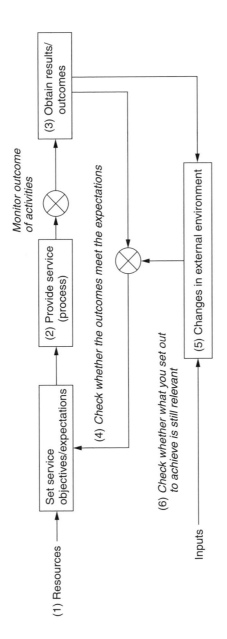

Figure 5.3 Double feedback loop.

particular medication). This extraction can be further modified by other data items (e.g. age, gender, data or episode).

Consider the following example. A topic audit of patients admitted to hospital with localised osteoarthritis of the pelvis is being undertaken. The first requirement is to identify patients who meet this criterion by means of a simple enquiry based on diagnosis. Information that is readily available from electronic sources may refine the criteria (e.g. length of stay of patients with complications recorded). Figure 5.4 demonstrates how this information can be presented to show how the length of stay of individual patients varies from that which is expected.

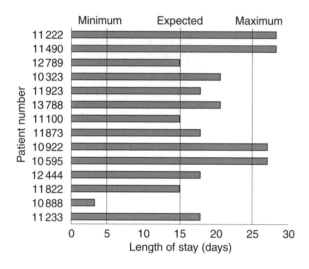

Figure 5.4 Topic audit: length of stay of patients with localised osteoarthritis of the pelvis.

It might be expected that, following identification of the patients and their basic details from operational information systems, further details of some of the patients would be taken from the medical records. For example, the audit may be focused on those patients who have a greater length of stay than the expected maximum (in this case, the few patients who are clearly outliers).

Statistical audit

Certain expectations can only be expressed as a percentage of the group, rather than as an expectation for any individual within that group. For example, a profile can be set for the percentage of patients undergoing a particular operative procedure who are expected to acquire infection. The number of actual acquired infections in this group can be compared with this figure, providing a simple but effective measure of performance in this area.

A good example of the use of statistical audit to analyse practice was in the case of the Shipman Investigation. In January 2000, Dr Harold Shipman, a GP from Hyde, Greater Manchester, was convicted of the murder of 15 of his patients.

Example 5.7 The Shipman Investigation

Source: Harold Shipman's clinical practice
1974–98
A clinical audit commissioned by the Chief Medical Officer, Department of Health., January 2001

An audit of this exceptional case was conducted by Professor Richard Baker of the Clinical Governance and Research and Development Unit in the Department of General Practice and Primary Health Care at the University of Leicester.

In total, 24 years of Harold Shipman's practice were reviewed. The audit revealed evidence of a higher number of deaths than would be expected, not just in the most recent years.

The main excess of deaths was among elderly female patients.

Part of this audit was conducted using readily available information from Medical Certificates of Cause of Death (MCCDs) in comparison with total practice records.

Information of interest routinely notified to National Statistics included the following:
- GP signing MCCD
- patient's name, age and sex
- place of death
- usual address
- certified cause of death.

In order to judge whether the number of deaths certified by Shipman was unusual, the expected numbers were required. Information for other GPs in the same locality was included for comparison.

In this comparison, Shipman issued 499 MCCDs. The next highest number for the same period by an individual GP was 210. There could be various explanations for the differences that would need to be ruled out, including the following:
- different profile (age, sex, etc.) and numbers of patients registered with practice
- differences in certification practice
- chance.

On further investigation these explanations were not found to be valid.

The Shipman case is exceptional, and a great deal of time and effort went into conducting what is a very robust and comprehensive audit, as is entirely appropriate to the shocking nature of the case. However, the information that was used to highlight an excessive number of deaths in the Shipman case is readily available. Routine electronic monitoring of all GPs could be undertaken. If this were done, it is possible that:

- this particular case would have been identified and investigated earlier

- poor performance (not due to illegal acts) could be detected and rectified.

On 14 January 2001, the *Sunday Times* newspaper (not the Department of Health) published the standardised mortality ratios for all of the hospitals in England. You may recall the previous discussion of standardised mortality ratios used in the allocation of revenue by means of the RAWP formula in the 1970s (*see* page 64 for 'Background to allocations'). Now there have been improvements in the accuracy of the data and refinement of the calculation, but this is not rocket science. These are relatively straightforward calculations that are made using readily available data.

Example 5.8 Comparing trusts

When comparing one hospital with another, it is essential to compare like with like. Crude death rates are not directly comparable. One hospital may admit a higher proportion of patients who are frail and elderly and who have more severe diagnoses. The rates are adjusted for age, sex, diagnosis, whether the patient was an emergency and the length of stay in the calculation of the hospital standardised mortality ratio (HSMR). A hospital with the national average number of deaths has an HSMR of 100. A higher figure indicates a higher number of deaths than expected. One encouraging finding of this study is that death rates are dropping by more than 2.5% per year. The HSMR was compiled from *Hospital Episode Statistics* by the Imperial College of Science and Technology and Medicine.

The five English trusts with the lowest mortality rates:
- University College London Hospitals (68)
- Bart's and the London Hospitals (70)
- Royal Free Hampstead (79)
- Royal West Sussex (81)
- Chelsea and Westminster Healthcare (82).

The five English trusts with the highest mortality rates:
- Walsall Hospitals (119)
- Mid Essex Hospitals (117)
- Sandwell Healthcare (117)
- Heatherwood and Wexham Park Hospitals (115)
- West Cumbria Healthcare (115).

Although there is some criticism of the formula used, particularly the fact that it does not take into account transferred patients, any hospital at the bottom of the list should be concerned and should be asking questions.

The only surprise is that hospitals in England were not aware of their mortality ratios and how these compared with those of other hospitals.

In these cases, it is the comparison of groups of patients with similar characteristics and clinical responses that allows any variation from the expected pattern to be identified. By using electronic means to set an expected level of occurrence or distribution and then comparing the observed occurrence or distribution against this, a wide range of factors can be easily monitored.

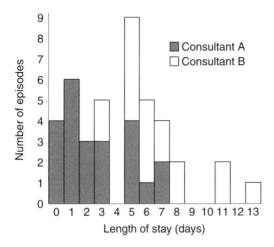

Figure 5.5 Length-of-stay distribution of angina patients for two consultants

The simple chart in Figure 5.5 provides a representation of the distributions that may be preferred by some observers. The same information can be conveyed by simple descriptive statistics, but is unlikely to have the same impact for those with a managerial background rather than a statistical one.

Figure 5.6 shows how the distribution of lengths of stay for two consultants varies. This may raise a number of questions that warrant further investigation.

- Are the clinical practices of both consultants appropriate?
- Do the patients included in the study represent a coherent group?
- Is the difference in distribution for the two consultants the result of different clinical practices or is it due to administrative differences?
- Can administrative processes for consultant B be improved without

adversely affecting the quality of clinical care of the patient while reducing the length of their stay?

- Do both consultants conform to best practice?
- Both consultants have patients with above the expected maximum length of stay. It might be of interest to investigate these particular patients to find out the reasons for this.

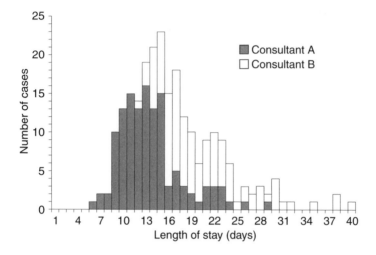

Figure 5.6 Length-of-stay distribution for primary replacement of major joints.

This is a fairly traditional view of quality assurance and how information might be used as part of that process – identifying exceptions, finding the reasons and eliminating them.

If the aim is to make improvements for the whole group, then a slightly different perspective is taken.

Figure 5.7 shows the original distribution of length of stay.

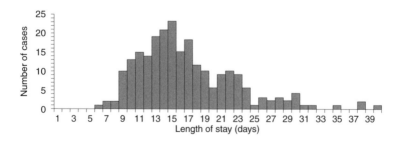

Figure 5.7 Original distribution.

The traditional approach of quality assurance suggests that the aim should be to reduce the length of stay of those patients with an exceptionally long stay (*see* Figure 5.8).

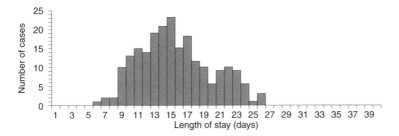

Figure 5.8 The traditional approach.

However, a continuous quality improvement approach suggests that a greater improvement for the whole group can be achieved by decreasing the overall range of length of stay (*see* Figure 5.9).

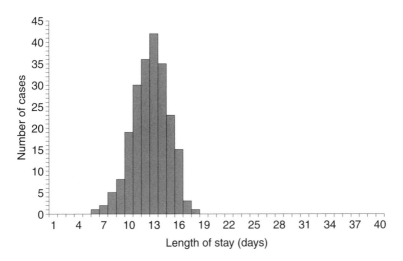

Figure 5.9 The continuous quality improvement approach.

Protocols to standardise both clinical and administrative processes can be used to achieve such improvements.

Management budgeting

As suggested previously, the management budgeting process of an organisation is a powerful way in which to influence the behaviour of those who commit resources within an organisation (*see* page 73 for 'Budgeting').

For the purposes of managing resources, the aims are:

- to place responsibility for managing a budget at the point where the commitment decisions are made for items covered by that budget

- as far as is possible, to make costs variable rather than fixed, so that they vary in relation to the activity that generates the cost.

In many of the new hospital projects under the Private Finance Initiative, where an external organisation owns the buildings and runs many of the non–clinical services, healthcare organisations tend to pay for the use of a facility on the basis of levels of activity. A larger proportion of the cost tends to be variable than in cases where the healthcare organisation owns the premises and operates all of the services. This has both advantages and disadvantages. Since perform-ance measurement is mainly based on activity, payment for usage allows a focus on managing that activity rather than managing overall costs. The risk associated with fixed items passes from the hospital to the supplier. However, the supplier will calculate costs to cover that risk and set charges accordingly.

The advantages can also be obtained within the organisation. For example, if general surgery has a budget for the radiology tests requested by the specialty, then those making requests will consider the clinical need and the relative distribution of resources within the specialty when making decisions to commit its resources. The radiology department will also have greater control over the re-sources that it manages, rather than having to cope with variable demand on a fixed budget.

Such a budgeting process requires the following:

- a schedule of prices for tests/requests, etc., based on the cost

- a means of transferring monies between budgets, based on activity.

This information is readily available in most healthcare provider organisations. However, there is a reluctance to implement such practices. Why is this?

- Is there a view that clinical decisions should not be influenced by cost?

- Is there a perception by Directors of Finance that lack of financial control would result?

> **Key points**
> - Quality and cost are not always in opposition. The evidence shows that high-quality care costs less than poor-quality care.
> - Clinical governance is the process that drives improvements in the quality of clinical care. As such it should also be the major driver for management of resources at the clinical level, and the driver of the associated information requirements.
> - Both prospective and retrospective information is important. Prospective information is used to 'get it right first time'. Retrospective information is used to detect cases where this did not happen.
> - Costing is an art, not a science. There is no such thing as 'the real cost'. The way in which costs are calculated depends on the purpose to which they are put.
> - Understanding cost at the level of patient group, and the ability to compare this with costs calculated in the same way in similar organisations, are essential to understanding and improving efficiency. Reducing individual budgets until the comfort level is unbearable is no longer an acceptable method for improving efficiency.
> - The preferred method for improving efficiency is through the design of effective processes, including the alignment of budgets to create appropriate incentives.
> - Linked case-mix classifications provide a framework for describing local health needs based on the right people having the right treatment in the right place, with the right funding and coming to the right conclusion.
> - Quality improvements require that outcomes are monitored against expectations, and that expectations are monitored against the changing environment to ensure that they are still valid.

References

1 Bullas S (1994) *Managing Hospital Quality and Cost: using patient-based information.* Longman, London.
2 Kohn L, Corrigan J and Donaldson M (eds) (1999) *To Err is Human.* Institute of Medicine, Washington DC.
3 Department of Health (1997) *The New NHS: modern, dependable.* The Stationery Office, London.
4 NHS Executive (1998) *Information for Health.* NHS Executive, Leeds.
5 NHS*Direct* online www.nhsdirect.nhs.uk
6 NHS electronic Library for Health; www.nelh.nhs.uk
7 NHS Information Authority; www.nhsia.nhs.uk
8 Batchelor GJ and Esmond JH (1989) *Maintaining High Quality Patient Care While Controlling Costs.* Healthcare Financial Management, Illinois.
9 Public Health Laboratory Service; www.phls.co.uk
10 Commons Public Accounts Committee; www.parliament.the-stationery-office.co.uk
11 National Institute for Clinical Excellence; www.nice.org.uk
12 National electronic Library for Health; www.nhs.uk/nelh/
13 Commission for Health Improvement; www.chi.nhs.uk

14 http://193.32.28.83/nhsexec/nhspaf.htm
15 http://193.32.28.83/public/nhssurvey.htm
16 Royal College of Nursing; www.rcn.org.uk
17 Department of Health (2000) *NHS Costing Manual*. Department of Health, London; www.doh.gov.uk/nhsexec/costing.htm
18 http://www.doh.gov.uk/nhsexec/refcosts.htm
19 National Audit Office (2000) *Hip Replacements: getting it right first time*. National Audit Office, London.
20 Bullas S (1989) *Casemix Management System Core Specification*. NHS Management Board, Resource Management Directorate, London.
21 Department of Health (1997) *Driving Efficiency in the New NHS*. Department of Health, London; www.doh.gov.uk/newnhs/exec/exec4~1.htm
22 Oakland JS (1999) *Statistical Process Control*. Butterworth-Heinemann, Oxford.
23 Bardsley M, Coles J and Jenkins L (eds) (1987) *DRGs and Health Care: the management of casemix*. King Edward's Hospital Fund, London.
24 NHS Management Board (1986) *Resource Management Health Notice (86) 34*. NHS Management Board, London.
25 Sanderson HF and Andrews V (1984) *Monitoring Hospital Services: an application of DRGs to hospital discharge data in England and Wales*. Occasional paper. London School of Hygiene and Tropical Medicine, London.
26 Wickings I, Childs T, Cole J and Wheatcroft C (1985) *Experiments Using PACTs in Southend and Oldham HAs. Final Report*. CASPE, London.
27 Sanderson H, Anthony P and Mountney L (eds) (1998) *Casemix For All*. Radcliffe Medical Press, Oxford.
28 www.casemix.nhsia.nhs.uk
29 www.leeds.ac.uk/nuffield/infoservices/UKCH/home.html
30 www.scotland.gov.uk/library3/health
31 www.scotland.gov.uk/libary3/health/afoq-05.asp
32 National Centre for Health Outcomes Development (1999) *Clinical and Health Outcomes Knowledge Base*. National Centre for Health Outcomes Development, London.
33 Lakhani A (2000) Assessment of clinical and health outcomes within the National Health Service in England. In: D Leadbeter (ed.) *Harnessing Official Statistics*. Harnessing Health Information series. Radcliffe Medical Press, Oxford.
34 Bullas S, Kwo D, Lowson K and Sanderson H (1994) *Conceptual Framework for Clinical and General Management*. Proceedings of the Twelfth International Congress of the European Federation for Medical Informatics.

6 Managing processes and change

Introduction

Change and modernisation have moved to the top of the NHS agenda. Health services are being pressured from every quarter – politics, technology, legislation and society – to meet new expectations for streamlined, responsive and effective delivery. The real challenge is not just to see that change is needed, nor even to understand the direction to take. It lies in making change happen in practice, over the long haul. It involves mobilising health service staff to be partners in stimulating and implementing solutions, rather than being dragged along as unco-operative and disgruntled workhorses.

There are many barriers to change. The change agenda in the NHS is large and is often seen by workers as too fragmented, unpredictable and complex to manage. The goalposts for performance are continually being moved. Operational issues such as meeting waiting-lists and revenue targets take priority. The information infrastructure is still immature and underdeveloped. Staff who are key to the change process move on, leaving skills and knowledge shortfalls in their wake. Important elements of the organisational structure are constantly being shuffled about.

However, while change is uncomfortable and often unpredictable, it is manageable if new and more efficient ways of working are designed. This does not need to entail a wholesale and risky upheaval of the entire organisation. Rather it needs a selective, incremental and continuous reshaping of processes which, over time, can create a new organisational culture. If an organisation cannot take up this management challenge, it will remain chained to past practices, and will risk demoralising the most important resource of all – the workforce.

This chapter describes some practical approaches to identifying the need for change, and managing and implementing change, in a measured and structured fashion. It defines some key principles in the change process, including the use of information as a driver and guide for change, and it gives examples of process change from contemporary NHS practice which have led to significantly improved resource use and patient outcomes.

Where to start?

No system is perfect, and that includes health systems. In other industries there are examples of bold commitment to redress quality and process defects where they occur, one example being the Land's End mail-order company whose catalogue promises 'Guaranteed. Period'.[1] This company is prepared to give an open-ended absolute guarantee of quality. Healthcare providers, on the other hand, have been less comfortable with such promises and guarantees. Nonetheless, healthcare providers do seek change in reaction to major problems, although not always in productive and constructive ways.

This is because managers and clinicians do not always have a clear idea as to whether these problems are occurring as a result of some special cause that is not part of the usual system of production, or whether the problems are occurring randomly as a characteristic of the process of production itself.

There are a large number of texts and techniques that provide exhaustive coverage of these issues and their application to health systems. They generally build on the work of Walter Shewart,[2] a statistician and physicist who worked on quality management in industry, and his student W Edwards Deming,[3] who, in the 1930s and for 40 years thereafter made a number of key observations that remain highly relevant to health systems today. These can be summarised as follows.

- Rates of failure, product by product, interval by interval (e.g. in such areas as hospital-acquired infections, prescription administration, mammography image quality, etc.), follow a relatively orderly mathematical distribution which can be easily graphed and modelled.
- These failure rates remain stable over time.
- They are a highly predictable characteristic of the process of healthcare production itself.

Shewart and Deming also secondly observed something in industry which is common in health systems today, namely that managers respond in highly inefficient ways to these failure rates, and may even exacerbate the problem. They tend to treat every failure or problem as if it had a special cause or was the responsibility of individuals, ignoring the fact that what they are seeing is the result of the overall process of production. By ignoring this fact and reacting on a case-by-case basis, they are wasting energy and resources. This destructive reaction is also not unusual at the political level, further confounding the management task.

Thirdly, Shewart and Deming noted that as a consequence of this behaviour, the production system, unable to correct the failure rates of its own work, becomes caught in an unhealthy cycle of regulation and inspection as the only recourse for protecting the customer, thereby adding considerable cost and waste to the production process.

Shewart proposed an alternative way of grappling with the issues.

- Managers (and clinicians) must be able to classify accurately the practice and process variations that they observe.
- When these variations are truly of special cause – due to events that are not part of the usual system of production – workers should be supported in correcting those special circumstances.
- When failure rates are random, and a fundamental characteristic of processes, then only changes in those processes can produce sustained reductions in failure rates.

These statistical and economic views imply that improvement and redesign – *process changes*, not just standardisation and control of variability – are essential activities for managers in complex systems such as healthcare.

References on statistical tools for mapping and analysing process variability (*statistical process control*), methods for testing and optimising the performance of a process, product or service (*design of experiments* approaches) and methods for supporting fault tolerance design, testability, safety, logistical support and related functions (*failure modes and effects analysis*) are provided in the Bibliography (*see* page 173).

Key change concepts

Bainbridge has identified a set of important foci for the effective management of change.[4]

129

Process

A process is a series of actions or steps which takes inputs and converts them into outputs. Examples of a *clinical process* include ordering a pathology test and admitting patients to hospital. An *administrative process* might include developing a new human resource policy for managing sickness absences, or a system for scheduling patients on to an operating-theatre list.

Components of process

The components of a process are shown in Figure 6.1. This conversion from input (ordering a pathology test) to output (test report) is undertaken through *resources* (e.g. people, communicating with each other and using technology, information, procedures, plant and equipment), working within certain *guidelines and rules* (quality accreditation standards for pathology machines, authorisation rules for ordering tests, performance targets for delivering timely results).

Taking the pathology ordering process as an example, the process steps for converting inputs to outputs might be depicted as shown in Figure 6.2.

Change and design principles

There are no simple short-cuts to designing and implementing process changes, but there is a basic and intuitively logical model which can be broken down into discrete stages as follows.

- *Identify the problem*: large problems are generally obvious, but as we have seen above, in the absence of information which tells managers and clinicians whether the problem is due to special effects or to the underlying production process, targeting the appropriate response is not always easy. The examples in the next section demonstrate some practical ways of tackling into this first step.

- *Design*: having identified the problem, it is then necessary to identify new requirements, first at the overall process level, and then for every component of the process to check that the various mechanisms integrate to meet requirements.

- *Describe and document* so that requirements are defined in sufficient detail to permit detailed development and building in the subsequent stages.

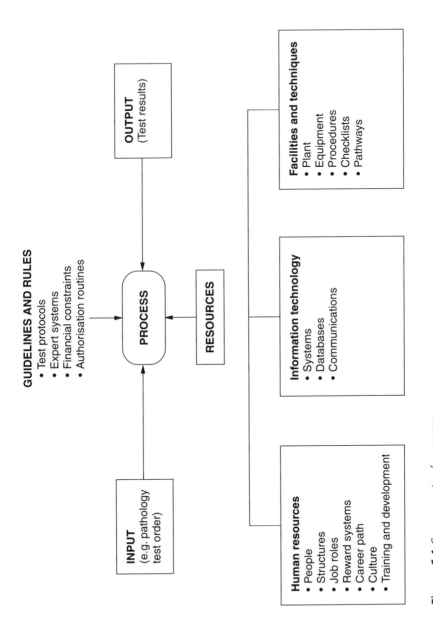

GUIDELINES AND RULES
- Test protocols
- Expert systems
- Financial constraints
- Authorisation routines

INPUT
(e.g. pathology
test order)

PROCESS

OUTPUT
(Test results)

RESOURCES

Human resources
- People
- Structures
- Job roles
- Reward systems
- Career path
- Culture
- Training and development

Information technology
- Systems
- Databases
- Communications

Facilities and techniques
- Plant
- Equipment
- Procedures
- Checklists
- Pathways

Figure 6.1 Components of a process.

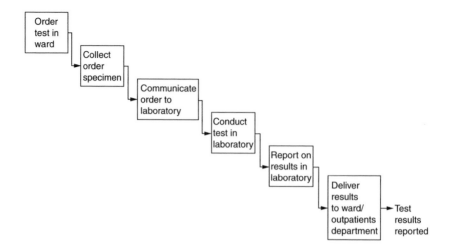

Figure 6.2 Examples of high-level process steps for pathology.

- *Develop, build and simulate/pilot* the establishment of new capabilities such as new organisational structures, training programmes, information systems and pathways, and the testing of these in a simulated or pilot environment.
- *Convert* existing routines to the new ones, and eliminate redundant or unhelpful practices, rules and constraints.
- *Implement*: translate new processes and capabilities into the workplace.
- *Monitor and evaluate* to assess the success of the changes.

An overview of the design and change principles is shown in Figure 6.3.

Some change examples

Improved patient treatment

Background

A 52-year-old man was admitted at 4a.m. through Accident and Emergency with haematemesis and a low haemoglobin level suggesting a bleeding peptic ulcer. The patient was clerked by the medical resident, who discussed the problem with the consultant physician on call, and an endoscopy was ordered immediately. The resident checked the roster of gastrointestinal physicians on call, but was unable to locate a gastroenterologist. She telephoned the surgical

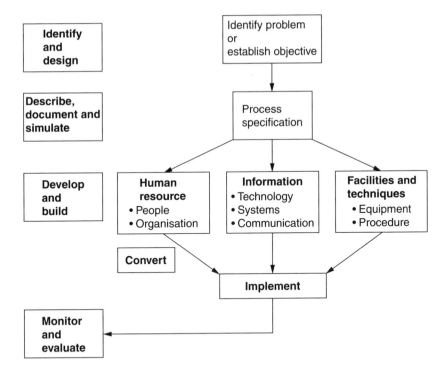

Figure 6.3 Overview of design and change principles.

Resident Medical Officer for advice, and he indicated that he was unable to undertake this procedure. Hesitant to refer this impasse back to the consultant physician on call, the resident commenced transfusion and quarter-hourly observations, but otherwise left the patient to be dealt with by the incoming staff on the morning roster at 9a.m. The patient survived, but lodged a complaint about the inadequate and untimely care provided.

The problem

The hospital's initial response was to seek to discipline the resident. It sought to treat the problem as arising from some special cause (the individual), rather than as a function of the underlying process for on-call support for junior staff. Senior managers were largely unaware of the underlying process, and had no systematically assembled information on which to make a judgement about what type of problem it was.

More detailed investigation included the following:

- a review of the hospital's switchboard arrangements for identifying and locating staff on call
- identifying responsibility for co-ordinating rosters and advising the switchboard of personnel 'swaps' and changes
- the response time for answering bleepers by those on call
- the 'rules' and conventions governing when on-call residents sought advice and attendance from on-call registrars and consultants.

This revealed the following set of ad hoc arrangements and processes.

- No single person was responsible for co-ordinating rosters.
- Junior staff did not feel personally responsible for notifying roster changes to the switchboard.
- The switchboard was under pressure, being inundated by multiple paper rosters in different formats for each speciality.
- On-call staff did not always answer their bleeper.
- There were different and conflicting conventions with regard to when senior staff wished to be called, or indeed permitted junior staff to wake them up, over and above the industrial regulations.

Interestingly, many of the consultants who were interviewed failed to appreciate the potential for adverse clinical incidents that these ad hoc arrangements fostered.

Design requirement

Administrative processes were needed to co-ordinate and standardise arrangements for appropriately supporting junior doctors when they are on call, and were also required for supervising treatment for seriously ill patients.

Solution

Because of the lack of appreciation of the flaws in the existing arrangements, the response was first to develop a simulation model (a statistical process control chart) based on real cases, but using the ad hoc arrangements and 'rules of engagement' that were already in place. This demonstrated to clinicians the number of 'near misses' over a six-month period that had been avoided by sheer luck, and those that had resulted in clinical incidents. Secondly, the proposed administrative process changes were negotiated with clinicians and the switchboard, and inserted into the simulation model to demonstrate over time how these changes could avert near misses and incidents. Armed with this 'pilot', the necessary changes were implemented, and they are now being monitored over time, again using statistical process control charts.

Results

The results to date show a significant decline in the rate of 'near misses'.

Analysis

Difficulties still exist in reinforcing the new arrangements. It is easy for busy individuals to slip back into long over-learned patterns of behaviour, and senior staff still show some reluctance to come into the hospital when junior staff need active assistance. Continuous monitoring and the provision of monthly process control data are essential for demonstrating variations from the average.

Improved patient outcomes

Background

In June 1999, the Department of Health published its first set of high-level clinical indicators of hospital quality for England during 1997–98.[5] One of those indicators, namely deaths in hospital within 30 days of emergency admission with a hip fracture, was of particular concern to 'Mossvale' Trust, a 600-bed acute hospital. The hospital's performance on this indicator showed that its age- and sex-standardised case fatality rate for hip fractures was the highest in its hospital cluster, and significantly worse than the average rate for other similar hospitals. The regional office and health authority required the trust to identify the problems and rectify them promptly.

Problem

Discussion between the Medical Director and the trauma surgeons, clinical practice manager and ward sister revealed a common perception that patients with hip fractures were experiencing considerable delays in getting to theatre, but a poor understanding of the precise nature of the delay, the factors contributing to it, and the impact on patients. Trauma clinicians tended to regard the problems as arising from poor theatre management, whereas theatre managers thought that the trauma surgeons were at least partly responsible because of their late operating start times, and their idiosyncratic changes to patient lists in mid-session. A retrospective audit of patient records revealed a series of process problems, including the following:

- delays from Accident and Emergency admission and being allocated a bed (median wait 2.8 hours; maximum wait 7.3 hours)
- 18% of patients waited more than 24 hours for their operation, with an unacceptable proportion waiting for up to four days
- an unacceptable proportion of delayed and cancelled operations led to prolonged starving and repeated starving preoperatively.

These findings were confirmed by a process-mapping analysis of hip fracture patients from admission to discharge, using the process redesign steps described previously.

Design requirement

Administrative and clinical processes were needed to accelerate the patient's 'journey' from admission to treatment in theatre.

Solution

Using the report *Hip Replacements: getting it right first time,*[6] the trust's clinical change team in collaboration with trauma staff designed, developed and built the following:

- a fast-track protocol to refer patients through Accident and Emergency to a specially designated assessment unit within a maximum of two hours
- a new integrated care pathway and surgical protocol to apply in the assessment unit with a target of 80% of patients to theatre within 24 hours, and 100% within a maximum of 48 hours
- patient access to a comprehensive elderly care service, which included a geriatrician, elderly care co-ordinator and specialist rehabilitation unit in the local community hospital
- a revised incident-monitoring form to provide timely feedback to staff, including the monitoring of infections
- a patient information booklet incorporating the care pathway was written, for patients and their carers to be given on admission.

The design-to-build stages of the project lasted six months, from initial identification of the problem to completion of documentation of the processes and pathways.

Results

The results have been less promising than expected, despite the excellent developmental work by the trauma clinicians, nurses and managers, and delays in admission to theatre are still being experienced.

Analysis

This partial result is occurring because a comparable effort was not expended on the theatre element of the process, to identify and analyse their problems in detail and to tailor solutions that link the front end of the process (admission) through the middle (the operative procedure) to the back end (postoperative treatment, rehabilitation and discharge). Work now needs to be directed towards understanding the production process in trauma theatres, mainly in order to assess the productivity throughput and the management routines that underpin this.

Efficiency and improved patient outcomes: collaboration between the acute and primary care sectors

Background

The Cancer Services Collaborative commenced in November 1999[7] as a Government-sponsored project to improve treatment and outcomes for cancer patients in the NHS. There was a general recognition that patients with suspected cancer were experiencing significant and unacceptable delays from the date of their referral to a specialist to the date of their first definitive treatment and, within that cycle, from the initial referral to the first specialist consultation, and thence to the first diagnostic investigation and on to treatment (surgery, chemotherapy, radiotherapy, etc.).

Design requirement

A referral and administration system was needed that guaranteed cancer patients a better co-ordinated and speedier journey, with the prospect of improved outcomes and more certainty and choice.

Solution

There are 51 project teams within nine cancer networks around the country working to achieve these goals, assessed against the following two standard measures:

- time (total number of days, including weekend days) from date of referral by any route to the date of first definitive treatment
- the percentage of patients who are pre-booked or scheduled for first specialist consultation, first diagnostic investigation and first definitive treatment.

When choosing the change approach and method for this ambitious project, the Cancer Collaborative adopted the US Institute for Healthcare Improvement (IHI) model advocated by Don Berwick, the IHI Chief Executive. This model is itself an adaptation and extension of the Shewart cycle of Plan–Do–Check–Act (PDCA), first articulated in 1931,[8] which relies on the principle that in order to improve, it is necessary to find a good idea and to test it. For the Cancer Collaborative, this model is expressed as Plan–Do–Study–Act (PDSA), as shown in Figure 6.4.

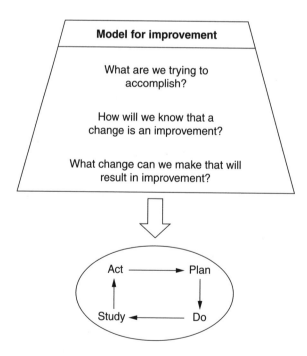

Figure 6.4 Plan-do-study-act model for the Cancer Collaborative.[9]

Yet as Berwick himself observes,[1] however much medicine espouses continuous learning as a core value, in practice PDCA cycles are rather rare in healthcare organisations. In most hospitals, even relatively routine procedures such as medication dispensing, physician rounds, record keeping and patient discharge remain unchanged for decades.

Results

This conservatism notwithstanding, the Cancer Collaborative has achieved some remarkable successes using the PDSA method. These are detailed in their report on the first 12 months of effort.[9]

Analysis

By adopting a process-control methodology with continuous information feedback, plenty of teamwork and process mapping to generate ideas, high visibility and vision sharing, and a learning and developmental approach, the Cancer Collaborative has demonstrated that major changes can be made to major process and production problems. The challenge is to extend these methods as depicted in Figure 6.5 into the next stage for this project, and to accelerate their uptake in other areas of healthcare.

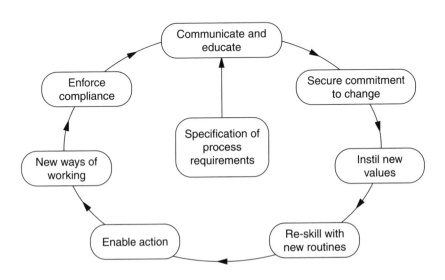

Figure 6.5 Process-led culture change.

Whole-system change

Background

'Austinfields' Trust is in the process of seeking approval for a PFI capital bid to build a new hospital with 900 beds. The philosophy of care underpinning its service provision in the new hospital – at least five years away from commissioning – is one of whole-system approach with an expanded and more effective Accident and Emergency/assessment front end, fast referral to the appropriate specialty for acute treatment, much more extensive use of intermediate-care beds, and significantly increased day-case activity.

Problem

The trust has a problem with its culture. Management structures are of the traditional command-and-control variety, there is limited multiprofessional team-working, and communication is patchy. Clinical staff are generally negative and passive ('why bother – we'll never get a new hospital anyway'), and there is a pervasive sense that things cannot be changed. This passivity stems partly from their perception that management has relentlessly driven activity, throughput and financial balance at the expense of quality. The negative response of clinicians is expressed in a lack of responsibility and accountability ('it's not my job to worry about reporting or fixing problems').

Design requirement

A culture is needed in which staff are more receptive to new ideas and more imaginative and flexible in their responses, and which ensures that staff go out of their way to meet the patient's needs rather than their own.

Solution

Because of the difficulties in convincing staff that a new hospital was in prospect, with a need to contemplate seriously the configuration of a new facility and the underpinning philosophy of care that would determine that configuration, a decision was taken to step in at the deep end and get staff into groups to specify the way in which they would like to work *if only they could have a new hospital*.

Staff were invited to nominate people in their work area (Accident and Emergency staff, theatre staff), employment category (cooks, domestics, estates management) or cross–hospital functions (informa-tion and telecommunications, human resources) to sit on working groups to specify their current working processes, and then to specify how these would change in a new hospital. Cross–linked member-ship was arranged where this was important. In total, 47 groups were commissioned over a period of six months, working within a structured framework and agenda, to undertake this task. After a slow start–up and some dispute within a number of groups, a pattern emerged whereby new philosophies of care were debated and absorbed, a new and common vocabulary developed around these principles and values, and a recognition of the future possibilities for a new hospital was distilled.

Group presentations of their discussions revealed a number of insights:

- the sharing of what people actually did in the hospital – a revelation for many
- the extent of engagement of staff in the process, and the palpable excitement which the opportunity for involvement had generated
- delight about the overwhelming number and range of excellent ideas and specifications for change and development
- the expectation that these ideas would be acted upon by senior management as the new hospital development took shape.

Results

This hospital has taken the first steps in a process–led culture change. It has used the need to specify new process requirements as a way into communicating with staff and educating them about the new care philosophy, securing commitment to change, and starting to instil new values. Having got this far, it is now confronting some tough calls. Having generated expectations, it now has to commence the long migration from the 'old' ways of doing business to its new model of care. This has to start quickly if it is not to lose the enthusiasm and good will of staff who have put effort into designing the changes they would like to achieve, but who need new skills and routines to enable definite action. This will require a two–pronged approach. Those teams which have well–established, functional and effective working processes need to be supported to start the migration now to keep the momentum going. Those with problems will need some intensive input from the change management team using the methods described above, to tackle their immediate problems before they can approach the migration highway's slip-road. Above all, the senior management of this hospital needs to harness the good will and expectations it has created, and use the good ideas generated thus far to take the next steps.

Analysis

Whole-system changes require some bold and decisive interventions to make the culture receptive to deploying the change models described so enticingly in the text-books. Staff do have good ideas – and they need an environment in which they can take some risks in exploring them.

The future for change

The NHS has one particular feature that differentiates it from private-for-profit industries, and which is both a major strength and sometimes a weakness. It has a very large workforce which is strongly committed to a set of public good principles and values, and which is not motivated entirely or mainly by financial incentives. This means that most people actually want to serve patients and do the best for them, and are prepared to adapt and change to further those values. However, one result of this commitment to NHS values is that some workers have a very strong allegiance to past practices, simply by virtue of having had to fight to retain them in a changing world. This can make the pursuit of positive change difficult, although by no means impossible if the right approaches are adopted.

There is much that is worth nurturing and preserving in the NHS, but like all health systems, there are many processes that are out-moded and which serve neither patients nor staff well. As we move increasingly into the light of public scrutiny, and have to deal with and respond to expectations of improved quality, we will need to familiarise ourselves with the tools and techniques that assist change and adaptation.

Fortunately, there are plenty to choose from. However much the health service shies away from any analogy between its production processes and those of other industries, there are striking similarities. This means that there is nearly 100 years' worth of experimentation and learning in industry that can be drawn upon, learned from and applied to health systems in many different and unique ways, in order to improve quality.

In order to gain maximum advantage from the available approaches and techniques, the NHS will need to recruit new skills into its workforce, and re-skill existing staff to use them effectively. These skills are largely in the areas of statistical information analysis and applied change management. The information is available – it just needs to be used better.

Key points

- Change and the need for continuous renewal are ever present features of all health systems.
- The very complexity and scale of the change agenda in the NHS make it difficult for NHS staff to embrace change willingly without encouragement.
- There are many obstacles in the way of change, including operational priorities, information shortfalls, shifting performance goalposts and staff changes.
- A number of different but complementary approaches can be deployed to assist change without necessitating wholesale upheaval in the organisation.
- Most of these involve the analysis and redesign of clinical and administrative processes.

References

1   Brennan TA and Berwick DM (1996) *New Rules: regulation, markets, and the quality of American health care.* Jossey-Bass Publishers, San Francisco, CA.

2   Shewart W (1931) *Economic Control of Quality of Manufactured Product.* Van Nostrand Reinhold, New York.

3   Deming WE (1986) *Out of the Crisis.* Massachusetts Institute of Technology – Centre of Advanced Engineering Study, Cambridge, MA.

4   Bainbridge C (1996) *Designing for Change: a practical guide to business transformation.* John Wiley & Sons, New York.

5   NHS Executive (2000) *Quality and Performance in the NHS: NHS performance indicators.* NHS Executive, Leeds.

6   Comptroller and Auditor General (2000) *Hip Replacements: getting it right first time. Report by the Comptroller and Auditor General.* The Stationery Office, London.

7   Delivering the NHS Cancer Plan; http://www.doh.gov.uk/cancer

8   Shewart W (1986) *Statistical Methods from the Viewpoint of Quality Control.* Dover Publications Inc., New York.

9   The Cancer Services Collaborative (2000) *Twelve Months On.* NHS Executive, Leeds.

7 Performance management and performance review

Introduction

Measuring performance is not new to health systems, and particularly not to hospitals where, unlike primary care or population health programmes, it is relatively easy to define the main output – the 'treated patient'. Typically we do this by describing and classifying the patient's problem (the patient demographics and diagnoses) together with the treatment response within a given care episode. Yet even in hospitals, performance measurement has sometimes had a troubled history, and the results have not always been applied thoroughly and practically to bring about change.

Some important developments

Florence Nightingale, for example, classified each patient who was discharged from her hospitals as being 'relieved of their symptoms, unrelieved or dead' – a telling measure of a simple outcome. This measurement continued in some hospitals until the 1950s when, regrettably, it fell into disuse until more contemporary approaches were adopted in the last two decades.

Florence Nightingale was not alone. In 1914, Ernest Codman, a surgeon at Massachusetts General Hospital in Boston, published *The Product of the Hospital*,[1] in which he argued that surgeons and organisations should be compared on their 'end results' as the foundation for improving care, and for giving patients access to information which helped them to choose between care providers.

Codman's argument, which was radical for its time and was largely rejected by his peers, drew on his discussions with industrial engineers, which led him to view hospitals as a complicated production system. From this he understood that if clinicians did not recognise and measure the effects of their treatment on patients (in much the same way that manufacturing industry was starting to assess the impact of the management of production lines on product quality), they were likely to be wasting resources and impairing quality.

Other international researchers in the 1950s, such as Paul Lembcke[2] from Johns Hopkins Medical School in Boston, formalised Codman's approach by proposing methods such as medical audit – a structured and rigorous data-driven method of comparing individual institutions and clinicians. According to Lembcke, comparative audits also had the advantage of identifying benchmark organisations whose performance standards others could strive to emulate.

Donabedian's 1966 publication, *Evaluating the Quality of Medical Care*,[3] proposed what many regard as the classic typology for performance and quality measurement and review. It was essential to measure and manage the following three elements of treatment and care:

- *structure* (how care delivery is organised)
- *process* (the functional operation of that structure)
- *outcome* (the result or visible effect of care).

During the 1980s, the NHS formulated performance measures using a prescribed set of indicators. The focus was on activity and costs, with less attention being paid to outcomes or useful measures of efficiency. The measures were based on readily available information from routine administrative data sets which themselves became increasingly more complicated over time.

According to one commentator, although these early NHS performance indicators were of some help to providers, planners and payers, they also led to some unintended behaviours such as 'tunnel vision, sub-optimisation, myopia, misrepresentation and gaming'.[4] Furthermore, they provided plenty of data but too little practical information. They tended to concentrate on activities that were easy to measure, rather than on outcomes that were important to patients, carers and professionals. Comparisons were difficult to make, and they presented an unbalanced picture of the NHS generally.

Example 7.1 Creating perverse incentives

Performance indicators created some perverse behavioural incentives, including means of achieving reductions in the size of waiting-lists and waiting-times, and perioperative mortality rates. Notable management responses have included queue-jumping 'easy' cases to reduce waiting numbers more quickly, using proximity to the 18-month 'cut-off' point as the sole criterion for urgent admission (as opposed to clinical need), removing patients from inpatient waiting-lists by redesignating the procedure as an 'outpatient procedure', and running a parallel waiting-list that is not included in the official statistics. There is some anecdotal reporting of clinicians risk-skimming less severe and complex patients to reduce their perioperative case fatality rates.

In the UK as in other developed health economies, there has been much debate about how best to define 'performance':

1   from whose perspective:
    • to what end and for what purpose
    • using what information,

and (more practically):

2   the extent to which the quality of the available information can appropriately and usefully support any such evaluation, review or management insights.

Throughout these developments, there has been a sense that *measurement* was the keyword. The implicit assumption has been that if we can measure performance, somehow we can translate the insights that it brings into improved management of performance to achieve better outcomes for patients, or more efficient ways of delivering healthcare.

On the ground, we know that this is not always so. So where do we start in managing and measuring performance?

This chapter defines some basic and simple performance management and measurement concepts with a view to using them practically in the workplace. It gives examples of how to take these concepts and apply routine information to assess and manage performance. The next chapter describes some more detailed models and case studies in particular areas.

Some important definitions

Definitions used in performance management and performance review include the following.

- *Operational objective*: An objective or goal which drives an action, process, function or method of working. It concerns an immediate, day-to-day function of an organisation (e.g. to have no Accident and Emergency trolley waits in excess of eight hours).

- *Strategic objective*: An objective which drives a longer-term plan of action or policy over, say, a 3–5-year period (e.g. to have implemented an electronic patient record to level 5 by 2005).

- *Intermediate outcome*: The result or visible effect of an action or process sampled before the action or process is complete (e.g. a process milestone for in-year monitoring such as 'redesigning our theatre information system by June, to deliver information to allow us to improve our theatre productivity by 5% by the year end').

- *Final outcome*: The final result or visible effect of an action or process (e.g. survival rate, readmission rate, income/expenditure balance at the year end).

- *Output*: The product of a process or the quantification of that product (e.g. the power of an apparatus, a treated patient).

- *Performance indicator*: A measure, standard or target against which to assess performance results, taking into account the relevance, reliability, availability, robustness and clarity of the measure, standard or target as an indicator of performance.

- *Benchmark*: A standard or point of reference against which to measure.

- *Standard*: An authoritative statement of an acceptable and measurable level of performance. The result will be 'all or nothing' – either the standard is met or it is not. It will be demonstrated by valid research or recommended by an author-itative body.

- *Target*: In a situation where 100% conformity against an indicator is not expected, this is the definition of the goal required (e.g. 80% of patients meet indicator X). This can be pragmatically employed in an imperfect situation where evidence of improved perform-ance is being sought.

- *Cost minimisation*: Reducing to the smallest possible amount the price to be paid for the output.

- *Efficacy*: This addresses the question 'Can it work under ideal circumstances?' (e.g. does the treatment do more harm than good to patients *who fully comply* with the treatment regime?).

- *Effectiveness*: This addresses the question 'Does it work in practice?' (e.g. does the treatment *actually* do more good than harm to the patients to whom it is given?). It is the ability to produce a defined or desired effect.

- *Efficiency*: Achievement of an objective at minimum cost.

- *Evaluation*: Assessment or appraisal.

- *Performance review*: A general survey or assessment of the execution of a duty or capability at a given point in time.

- *Monitoring*: The act of measuring or checking on a person, device, situation, operation, etc.

- *Best practice*: This strikes a balance between quality, quantity and cost, and so involves a judgement, based on the available evidence, of an attainable goal.

- *Survey*: A straightforward review of the current situation, determining boundaries without testing against a standard or hypothesis; a data collection which is not measured against any criterion (e.g. may count frequency of occurrences, etc.). The intent may be to establish baseline data as a pre-audit activity.

- *Research*: A systematic process to extend the sum of knowledge using scientifically sound techniques and a testable proposition.

For background information and sources of definitions, see the list of references at the end of this chapter.[5–8]

Starting at the beginning: performance objectives

When considering the importance of setting clear objectives against which performance could be reviewed and monitored, Mark Twain's aphorism might be amended to: 'If you don't know where you're going, you won't know whether you got there'. It seems simple enough to apply this to healthcare, where the objectives and outcomes are obvious – heal the sick, alleviate symptoms, prevent illness and promote good health. However, measuring performance against these objectives is not always straightforward, and the results of healthcare interventions do not always deliver good outcomes.

> **Example 7.2** Learning from adverse events
>
> In a report by an expert group on learning from adverse events in the NHS,[9] evidence was presented that each year:
> - 400 people die or are seriously injured by adverse events involving medical devices
> - 10 000 people are reported to have experienced a serious adverse reaction to drugs
> - around 1150 people who have been in recent contact with mental health services commit suicide
> - the NHS pays out around £400 million a year in settlement of clinical negligence claims, and it has a potential liability of around £2.4 billion
> - hospital-acquired infections are estimated to cost the NHS nearly £1 billion, and around 15% of these cases may be avoidable
> - an estimated 850 000 adverse effects may occur, resulting in a direct cost of £2 billion in additional hospital days alone – around 50% of these cases might be avoidable.

If performance objectives are to be integral to day-to-day work and culture, they must be believed and 'owned' locally with strong staff buy-in. They must be useful and relevant to people's operational lives, while at the same time reminding them of the larger and longer-term agenda engaging the entire health system.

Each organisation therefore needs to take those objectives and targets that are relevant to their own service from the vast array of the Government's performance objectives, targets and priorities for services, finances and workforce that are set out in a number of policy documents, National Service Frameworks, NICE decisions and NHS circulars (summarised below). They need to translate them into relevant, useful and measurable local that are goals specific to their own services and programmes.

NHS performance objectives

Over the past three years, the NHS has worked hard to build a framework. This describes the following:

- performance 'objectives' for the health system
- the way in which these can be measured
- the way in which the measures can be used to review performance and manage it to best effect
- structure and incentives to bolster improved performance.

These are described in the following policy documents:

- *The New NHS: modern, dependable*[10]

- *A First-Class Service: quality in the new NHS*[11]
- *The NHS Performance Assessment Framework*[12]
- *Improving Working Lives*[13]
- *National Service Frameworks on Coronary Heart Disease.*[14]

The Performance Assessment Framework sets out six broad areas of measurable performance for the NHS, to which a seventh has since been added. These are shown in Figure 7.1.

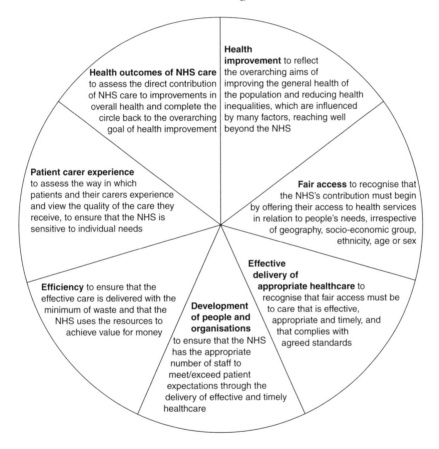

Figure 7.1 Seven areas of performance.

These performance areas and their objectives consist of a balanced mix of the following:

- population health improvement outcomes (e.g. age–standardised mortality rates from malignant neoplasms at the health authority level)

- process measures of fair access (e.g. percentage of adults registered with a General Dental Service dentist within the health authority)
- intermediate output measures of effective delivery (e.g. childhood immunisation rates by health authority)
- efficiency measures (e.g. day-case rates within hospitals)
- measures of patient satisfaction
- final outcomes (e.g. case fatality rates within hospitals).[15]

The Performance Assessment Framework measures are supplemented by numerous other performance targets laid out in specific NHS guidance circulars, National Service Frameworks, NICE decisions, Controls Assurance and Risk Accreditation registers, as well as by local targets set annually by regions or health authorities and/or primary care organisations in the Service and Financial Framework (SaFF) negotiations, and by those set within organisations as local goals. From 2001–02, many of these measures will be integrated and expressed for the wider health economy within Health Improvement Plans (HImPs). To these must be added performance objectives and targets for managing the NHS workforce and finances.

Making performance objectives 'real' in the NHS workplace

The annual performance planning cycle

Every year, great effort goes into negotiating funding allocations, activity level agreements, service developments and efficiency measures. The process spans at least five out of every 12 months, absorbs the time of many people and is a source of much angst and volumes of 'guidance' and paperwork. For many hard-pressed workers for whom the larger health system planning context is remote, and on whom the pressure to meet local income/expenditure and activity targets is relentless and paramount, the business of broader objective setting comes as an unwelcome distraction from the 'real business' of patient care.

Added to these pressures, each level of the NHS – the centre, regional offices, health authorities and service providers – may require different styles and approaches to business planning and objective setting. Not infrequently each imposes on providers additional local performance targets that do not always match up even within 'the patch'. This requires quite different performance reporting formats for each level of administration.

This is common across all developed health economies, simply because health systems are complicated, albeit highly organised and adaptive organisms. The practical survival trick for health providers in their business planning is to run several complex processes in parallel (the SaFF process and corporate objective setting), to map them against each other and to link them in a structured fashion at key points along the way.

The SaFF process is well developed, even if the details are not universally understood. SaFFs nest within and should give effect to organisational objectives which themselves need to be explicit and clearly relate to Government policy and performance targets. It is desirable that these objectives are developed in advance of the start of SaFF negotiations, and they should have been 'operationalised' (i.e. translated into practical actions and targets) down through the organisation to divisional, group, speciality or service level. Since this is not always practicable, the local development of initiatives relating to improved activity, how to deal with cost pressures, service developments and the like usually proceeds in tandem with the process of agreeing corporate objectives.

The annual planning cycle within an organisation would typically start in September/October each year, with calls for bids and plans for SaFF initiatives from divisions or services, against a parallel process which takes Government policies and targets and converts them, in the first instance, to high-level corporate objectives that are tailored to include local aspirations and circumstances. By December it should be possible to map the early SaFF initiatives to the corporate objectives, and then progressively fine tune each of them to bring them into alignment by March the following year.

Not all performance objectives and targets can be handled within this planning cycle. Government often introduces policy or legislation which needs to be accompanied by new or revised performance targets during the year, and these must be dealt with when they arise.

Developing high-level performance objectives within an organisation

Typically, an organisation will adopt a manageable number of high-level performance objectives (preferably no more than six to eight) that reflect its own priorities and intentions, as well as broader NHS aspirations. These must be linked both to the management structure and to the management process within the organisation, so that accountability for performance is clear and transparent.

It is easy to say that corporate objectives and their associated performance measures and targets should be 'owned' by staff, but much more difficult to achieve in practice. For all sorts of obvious reasons, staff need to sign up to these if their organisation is to demonstrate a high-performance culture. Signing up can only be achieved if staff are actively involved in developing objectives and if they believe that these are worthwhile and achievable – even at a stretch. Investment of time and effort in such bottom-up consultation is worthwhile, not only to deliver commitment to objectives and performance, but also because it is a springboard for several other Government objectives, including the following:

- the first stage of building individual performance and development plans
- inculcating among staff the principle that each person plays a vital role in making their bit of the health service responsive to patients.

Examples of local high-level organisational performance objectives which reflect broader NHS policy objectives might include the following:

- to demonstrate improved access to, and responsiveness of, patient care services
- to provide high-quality patient care
- to introduce improved care and treatment models which better serve patient needs
- to work with other health and social care agencies to deliver measurable service improvements to the local community
- to ensure a committed and motivated workforce
- to improve facilities and training programmes that enable better support for healthcare professionals in their delivery of patient care
- to demonstrate value for money to the public so that maximum capital and revenue are available to support patient care.

Sub-objectives: developing measurable actions/ targets within high-level objectives

Different levels of the organisation's structure and management will need to interpret and define the high-level objectives differently. Some objectives will be set at the corporate level, others will be more relevant at the divisional or individual service level, while yet others will be more appropriately defined for individuals.

Whichever level it is, each objective must be coupled with sub-objectives, preferably in the form of practical actions or performance targets that clearly give effect to, or indicate delivery of, each high-level objective. It is essential that these targets and the results of actions are measurable over time, or at particular points in time (e.g. by July, 50% of staff in the division, group or ward will have completed their individual performance and development appraisal, with 100% completed by October).

Measuring performance

It is a general rule of thumb that you cannot manage what you cannot measure. Thus if you cannot measure performance easily, using routinely available and reliable information or some other form of process 'milestones', then the likelihood is that performance will not be assessed at all. Each organisation's information infrastructure must be capable of delivering the required routine management information. This is not to say that we should only ever set objectives that are easy to measure. Some of the most important ones, such as the satisfaction of patients with the quality of service that is offered and provided, and some recent NSF targets, require a little more effort, such as the application of specific-purpose survey methods.

If surveys are to be reliable, valid and capable of repeat application year on year for comparing performance over time, they need sound technical and professional development and analysis. This is usually beyond the skills and budgets of individual organisations. A collective and common survey development co-ordinated by, say, a health authority in collaboration with the rest of the health community is a cost-effective route to take. It shares among organisations the cost of professional development, roll-out and analysis, including annual recalibration to take account of new developments and customised

155

requirements, and allows for both comparisons and year-on-year trends.

With these exceptions, the information for measuring the types of performance objectives described above is generally available in the NHS as a by-product of routine collections used in day-to-day operations. For hospitals, this is largely drawn from the patient administration systems (PAS), general ledger systems and personnel and payroll systems, and conforms to nationally agreed data standards. In primary care, access to reliable routine information is improving as the computerisation of GP practices accelerates. These major data sources are described comprehensively in the companion text *Harnessing Official Statistics.*[16]

Using these data sources, performance information can be readily assembled from routine information collections.

Other sources of information will also be crucial for performance management and review. These include clinical audit systems containing significantly more detailed patient information, adverse incident reporting and monitoring systems, complaints databases and legal claims registers.

Different ways of measuring performance

Not all performance actions, targets or results can be measured numerically. Some, such as 'Implement clinical governance performance and accountability structures', 'Implement a personal development and review system for all staff' or 'Develop a business case for an electronic patient record', are processes whose progress over time needs to be tracked developmentally using staged and agreed delivery milestones. This is illustrated in Table 7.1 below.

Table 7.1 Example of a high-level corporate objective and its sub-objective/action, measured as process milestones

Corporate objective	Sub-objective
Demonstrate improved access to, and responsiveness of, patient care services	Improve theatre utilisation by 5% to support the elective waiting-lists

Milestones

Quarter 1	Quarter 2	Quarter 3	Quarter 4
1 Agree a new strategy for Theatre Information System (TIMS) 2 Complete roll-out of TIMS 3 Develop a monthly reporting mechanism	1 Complete a three-month cycle of monthly data feedback to specialties 2 Agree target improvements and baseline performance 3 Improve data quality and completion	1 Monitor progress and agree action plans as necessary	1 Overall theatre utilisation improved by 5%

In this example, the anticipated performance measures are set out as quarterly process milestones, with a quantitative output only being achieved in quarter 4. This mix of measures is a common and very acceptable approach to apply.

Quantitative measures

Most measures of performance involve an element of comparison, and some require a translation of the information so that it adds value by making better sense to clinicians and managers. These include the following:

- time series – comparing today's level of performance with previous quarterly performance using the same measure for the same service (*see* Figure 7.2)

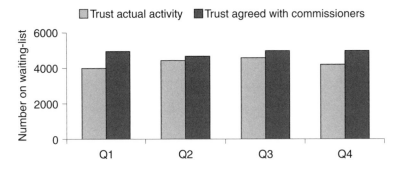

Figure 7.2 Trust actual waiting-list activity against agreed target (1999–2000).

- internal service comparisons – comparing one service's performance with another service's performance using the same measure
  (*see* Table 7.2 and Figure 7.3)

Table 7.2 Internal service comparisons

Performance indicator	Divisional update

1. Theatre utilisation improved by 5% by March 2002
(a) Baseline data for April 2001: theatre utilisation, 76% (excluding overruns)
(b) Target for March 2002: theatre utilisation, 81% (excluding overruns)
	Reporting function developed/purchased Information technology/information department input to support initiative
	Data completeness:
	  April 2001 (baseline), 64%
	  September 2001, 88%

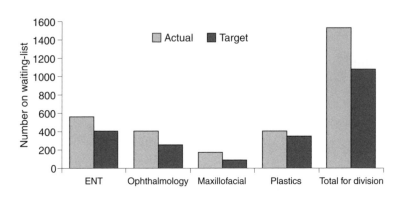

Figure 7.3 Elective waiting-list: actual activity against agreed target by speciality for first quarter (2000–2001).

- using external comparators – comparing performance between
  peer organisations using a common measure (e.g. percentage of
  outpatients seen within 30 minutes of their appointment time,
  local trust vs. other trusts) (*see* Figure 7.4)

- comparing performance against an externally validated 'gold standard' (*see* Table 7.3)

- comparing performance against an internally set benchmark (*see*
  Figure 7.5).
  Corporate objective: Ensure a committed and motivated workforce.
  Sub-objective: That 15% of the workforce should be recruited from
  the local ethnic minority population.

Table 7.3 Comparison of performance against a critical mass standard

Trust performance 1999–2000

Procedure/speciality/consultant	Elective	Non-elective	Total spells	Annualised spells	ALOS*	Deaths (n)	Mortality (%)	Critical mass**	Peer ALOS	Peer mortality
Amputations of leg								15	44.7	19.05
General surgery/Dr A	6	13	19	38	41.22	1	5.26			
General surgery/Dr B	3	2	5	10	47.20	1	20.00			
General surgery/Dr C	2	3	5	10	25.60	0	0.00			
General surgery/Dr D	1	3	4	8	18.25	0	0.00			
Plastic surgery/Dr E	0	2	2	4	28.00	0	0.00			
Trauma and orthopaedics/Dr F	0	1	1	2	61.00	0	0.00			
Trauma and orthopaedics/Dr G	0	1	1	2	73.00	0	0.00			

*Average length of stay.

**Critical mass is an externally validated 'gold standard', meaning that each consultant should be performing a minimum of 15 amputations of leg procedures each year in order to maintain competency.

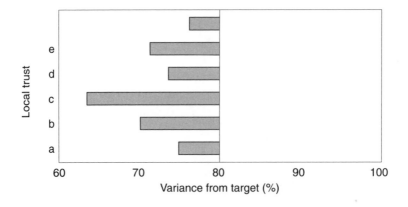

Figure 7.4 Total number of patients waiting in excess of 13 weeks by speciality for benchmark trusts (1999–2000): variance from target.

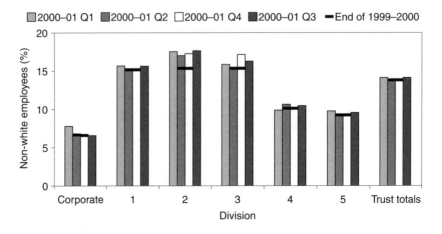

Figure 7.5 Ethnic minority composition of workforce 2000–2001, compared with 1999–2000.

Figure 7.5 shows that divisions 1, 2 and 3 have met the target of 15%.

- 'value-added' performance measures (e.g. applying additional dimensions to routine data to assist comparison, such as grouping detailed individual patient data into a health resource group to take into account differences in patient severity and complexity)
- individual consultant appraisal (*see* Figure 7.6).

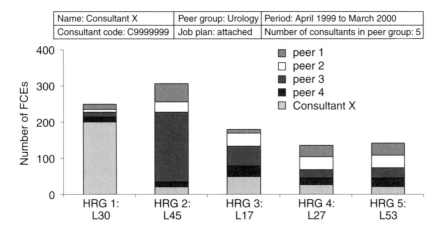

Figure 7.6 Individual consultant appraisal. Top five HRGs by volume for peer group (by number of finished consultant episodes).

Table 7.4 gives a key to the HRGs in Figure 7.6.

Table 7.4 Healthcare resource groups (HRGs)

HRG code	Description
L30	Prostate or bladder neck minor endoscopic procedure (male and female)
L45	Extracorporeal lithotripsy
L17	Bladder major endoscopic Px
L27	Prostate transurethral resection procedure > 69 with complications
L53	Renal general disorders < 70 without complications

Comparative data for peer organisations are generally available from health authorities and regional offices, because they collate information from all service providers in their locality. When selecting comparator organisations, care should be taken to ensure that sufficient similarity exists to allow valid comparison. For example, patient populations differ between hospitals. Not only might there be differences between metropolitan teaching hospital patient populations and populations in rural district hospitals, but even among the former there will be significant variations. Some do not treat any children or maternity cases, whereas others do. These differences will have a significant impact on mortality rates, and the data should therefore be standardised for age and gender.

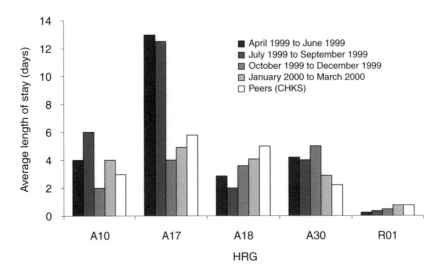

Figure 7.7 Top five elective HRGs (by volume of admissions) over the period 1999–2000.

Table 7.5 gives a key to the HRGs in Figure 7.7.

Table 7.5 Healthcare resource groups (HRGs)

HRG code	Description
A10	Peripheral nerve disorders < 70 with or without complications
A17	Cerebral degenerations < 70 with or without complications
A18	Multiple sclerosis or other CNS demyelinating conditions
A30	Epilepsy < 70 without complications
R01	Major spinal procedures

The Department of Health also publishes comprehensive performance assessment data in its annual publication, and this can be applied
readily for comparative use at hospital and health authority level,
with the usual provisos with regard to comparability. Some organisations subscribe to private data-processing companies, such as
CHKS, which provides a range of useful comparisons with peers
on activity and quality dimensions.

Using performance review to manage performance

Knowing the results of activities does not of itself lead to improved
performance. These results have to be measured, analysed and dis-

cussed with line managers and staff in ways that lead to a commitment to follow-up action. An effective process is needed that turns data into information as the basis for structured and constructive discussion between the analysts, clinicians and line managers.

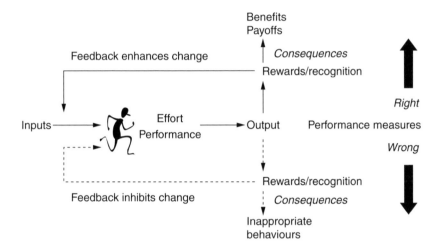

Figure 7.8 Performance review approach.

This process, as depicted in Figure 7.8, can be organised formally in a performance management and review, say monthly or quarterly, between senior executives, line managers and clinicians in each service area, or annually with individuals in the form of a performance development and review appraisal. The effort made by staff to produce measured outputs and performance needs to be recognised. If this effort is measured in the right way, and appropriate rewards are given, then the benefits of the review and feedback approach will include an enhanced performance culture.

Achieving commitment to change as a result of performance review is not straightforward. Logic is not always sufficient – people need incentives. Clinicians and managers in the NHS are smart – they can usually see the problems that lead to underperformance, but they don't always know how to fix them immediately. Technical assistance and training may provide part of the solution where work processes need to be redesigned, and sometimes extra resources need to be applied, but often healthcare workers can generate solutions if they are allowed a little 'headroom' to think and reflect, and if they are allowed to take some risks. This is the challenge for leaders in the NHS, and their response will determine whether or not there is a real commitment to improve performance.

The future for performance management and review

As in other countries and industries, performance management and review in the NHS will continue to expand and evolve. For the time being, a number of technical and delivery problems in the production of healthcare services have yet to be solved. Until governments are reassured that these are in hand, they will continue to manage the health service by telling service providers what to do and how to do it through the medium of an increasing number of precise performance targets. Assuming that confidence grows, and technology and people investments demonstrate that service delivery problems are being redressed, then the emphasis is likely to shift to the quality of management and organisation, with an increasing reliance on continuous quality improvement (in any of its various forms).

This development would be profoundly welcomed by clinicians, managers and patients, who would rightly see it as a coming of age for performance management in the NHS.

Key points

- Performance measurement has a long and commendable track-record in health systems.
- Designing business objectives against which performance is to be measured is the logical first step.
- The NHS has a well-established set of interlocking policies and performance frameworks which contain well-established performance objectives.
- These need to be localised in each healthcare setting, and measured systematically using readily available information.
- Performance results should be acknowledged and fed back to staff through constructive appraisal mechanisms which recognise effort and encourage further change.

References

1 Codman EA (1914) The product of a hospital. *Surg Gynecol Obstetr.* 18: 491–6.
2 Lembcke PA (1952) Measuring the quality of medical care through vital statistics based on hospital service areas. 1. Comparative study of appendectomy rates. *Am J Pub Health.* 42: 276–86.

3 Donabedian A (1966) Evaluating the quality of health care. *Milbank Mem Fund Q.* **44**: 166–203.
4 Smee C (2000) The Performance Assessment Framework: where did it come from and where is it going? In: *Health Care UK*. King's Fund, London.
5 Lugon M and Secker-Walker L (eds) (1999) *Clinical Governance: making it happen*. Royal Society of Medicine Press Ltd, London.
6 Godwin R, DeLacey G and Manhire A (eds) (1996) *Clinical Audit in Radiology: 100+ recipes*. Royal College of Radiologists, London.
7 Lack JA, White LA, Thoms GM and Rollin AN (eds) (2000) *Raising the Standard*. Royal College of Anaesthetists, London.
8 Drummond MF, Ludbrook A, Lowson K and Steele A (1986) *Studies in Economic Appraisal in Health Care. Volume 2*. Oxford University Press, Oxford.
9 Department of Health (2000) *An Organisation With a Memory*. The Stationery Office, London.
10 Department of Health (1998) *The New NHS: modern, dependable*. HMSO, London.
11 Department of Health (1998) *A First-Class Service: quality in the new NHS*. HMSO, London.
12 Department of Health (1998) *The NHS Performance Assessment Framework: a national framework for assessing performance*. The Stationery Office, London.
13 Department of Health (2000) *Improving Working Lives*. The Stationery Office, London.
14 www.doh.gov.uk/nsf/
15 Department of Health (2000) *Quality and Performance in the NHS: NHS performance indicators*. The Stationery Office, London.
16 Leadbeter D (ed.) (2000) *Harnessing Official Statistics*. Harnessing Health Information Series. Radcliffe Medical Press, Oxford.

8 Making it happen

Improve or go, Milburn tells hospital executives
By Jeremy Laurance, Health Editor
Independent, 26 September 2001
Alan Milburn, the Secretary of State for Health, told the chief executives of a dozen failing NHS trusts yesterday 'get your act together or face the sack'.

This was a response to the publication of the NHS Performance Ratings in September 2001, when Alan Milburn warned the 12 'worst' hospitals in Government league tables. This is not recognised as the best way to motivate chief executives and other staff working in some of the most complex organisations, especially when the improvements needed almost certainly require a change of culture and are demanded within months. The trusts were ranked on just nine targets, including waiting times, cancelled operations and cleanliness.

It will certainly focus minds on achieving very specific targets in the shortest time possible. The risk is that this will be achieved at the expense of those things that are more difficult to measure, particularly quality of care and clinical outcomes. It can potentially reduce overall performance by serving as a distraction from looking at the system as a whole and taking an integrated approach, which will result in long-term sustainable improvements. This is not to suggest that there is a choice – to meet short-term political targets *or* to make longer-term quality improvements. The challenge is to achieve both, and this can only be done by changing the way in which things are done – not only changing the processes but also changing the culture. Adopting an evidence-based approach is an essential element in achieving this.

This may appear to be asking the impossible. So in this final chapter we shall look at some important organisational considerations when adopting an evidence-based approach to managing resources, and how to get into a virtuous spiral of positive change.

Monitor what is happening

Much of this book has been devoted to gathering information in order to find out what is happening. For example:

- what the current levels of performance are, and how these compare with those of other organisations (*see* Chapter 7)
- whether there are 'hot-spots' of clinical quality that need immediate improvement (*see* Chapter 5)
- how much delivery of healthcare costs (*see* Chapter 5)
- how effectively finance is used to achieve ongoing operations and new developments (*see* Chapter 4)
- how efficiently the estate is being managed and supplies are being sourced (*see* Chapter 3)
- what the staff think (*see* Chapter 2).

And much more besides.

These chapters also covered the way in which information can be used to monitor developments and evaluate change – to know what impact actions are having.

In Chapter 6 we described an approach to managing processes and change. Change in the absence of a clear understanding of processes, particularly where these cross organisational boundaries, is likely to result in the following:

- problems arising in other parts of the organisation, giving an overall drop in performance
- staff retaining old processes as well as adopting the new ones to avoid these problems.

Making space

It is difficult to change the way in which things are done and to change the culture when the day-to-day pressures do not allow time to stand back and view what is happening or to think how things might be improved. People must be given space and time away from those pressures. 'Away-days' are a good idea, but are of limited use when those taking part are concerned about work piling up that they will need to tackle on their return.

A team whose members are drawn from the existing workforce, relieved of their operational duties and given a remit for change is better. This may be as a project team to undertake a specific, time-limited set of activities, or a more general resource for change. Given training in investigation, process development and change techniques, such a team can provide a force for change. It must be remembered that sustainable change cannot be imposed, even by an internal team.

Bringing in external help to work on specific issues or alongside an internal team can reduce the learning curve significantly, and may be more cost-effective in the longer term.

One of the most effective ways of finding space is to examine what makes you busy and use your time differently. The success of books and courses on time management is testament to the view that many managers could spend their time more effectively. Apart from formal meetings, many of a manager's activities only last a few minutes each. The job of a manager is often very fragmented, with frequent interruptions. Reduction of fragmentation and interruptions will allow periods of sustained concentration on more strategic activities.

An integrated strategic approach

Achieving the maximum benefit from activities to improve performance and create change requires an integrated strategic approach.

A common reason why benefits are not achieved is the inability to balance people, processes and information elements of operations or change.

A strategic approach establishes the following:

- an understanding of the baseline – the current position
- a clear view of the future position to be established and the objectives to be achieved
- the activities that are needed to close the gap between the current and future positions
- how it can be recognised that the end-point has been reached.

Measurement forms an important part of each stage.

Many healthcare organisations have used the Balanced Scorecard to help them to view problems from different perspectives, and to aid integration.[1]

People matter

There are few people in the NHS who don't want to improve the quality of care for patients, and to improve their contribution towards making this happen. There are also few people who don't have a good idea of where improvements could be made and some idea about how this might be achieved.

There are many who:

- are not clear about what the organisation expects of them
- have not had the training to undertake what is being asked of them
- do not know how what they do impacts on others within the organisation
- are not sure whether they would receive support if they spoke out.

On the latter point, they are more likely to believe that if they raised their head above the parapet, it would be shot off.

This is not an environment that is conducive to the achievement of positive change and improvement. The workforce really is the most valuable resource, and it is the key both to effective management of all other resources and to improving performance.

Culture of the organisation

Many management decisions are made by groups, not by individuals. The majority of the group and particularly influential individuals within it must value evidence if this approach is to stand a chance of becoming part of the culture. It is essential that evidence is sought, used in reasoned argument and valued by senior managers. Often it is opinion and influential personalities that are valued more than evidence to the contrary.

Organisations in which a 'blame culture' is predominant do not encourage people to come forward with information on what is actually happening. Staff will be more inclined to tell managers what they want to hear, rather than what is in fact happening. Much can be learned from failure as well as success, but in a blame culture no one is encouraged to admit failure, let alone discuss it.

Another aspect of culture is the 'not invented here syndrome', which discourages people from seeking out the experiences of other organisations. Funds are often available to develop new approaches or ideas, but there are few awards or investments for the application of developments from elsewhere.

When advocating an evidence-based approach, it is important to stress that current best evidence is required – the research base required for clinical evidence is rarely available. That evidence needs to be made available so that timely decisions can be made. A common means of avoiding making any decision at all is to agree to undertake further analysis or set up a group to investigate – 'paralysis through analysis' must be avoided.

Evidence needs to be made an integral part of the culture of the organisation. It is important that evidence is valued and its effective use is rewarded. This will be achieved when evidence is positively reflected in all aspects of the culture, including the following:

- routines and rituals (e.g. meetings and briefings)
- systems such as reporting on adverse events, budgets and rewards
- organisational structures and the more informal groups that make decisions
- power structures
- stories told by one member of staff to another or to new recruits and which reflect what is important to the organisation.

Conclusion

Getting the right resources in the right place at the right time to deliver high-quality clinical services is a major challenge for managers of healthcare services. This must be achieved in an environment where the demands for change are unprecedented, expectations are raised and evidence is accumulating at too fast a rate for experiential management to provide the levels of performance that are demanded. We argue that adopting an evidence-based approach is essential for effective management in this environment.

Effective use of evidence requires an awareness of what information is available and where it can be found when needed. The vast amount of information that is readily available makes it impossible to remember, and thankfully the easy access facilitated by technological advances means that this is no longer necessary. It also requires an enquiring mind, the 'information seeking' that we talked about in Chapter 1, together with an awareness that others may interpret the same information in different ways. In addition, it requires an awareness of the changing environment and a willingness to adapt practices to respond to that environment. Finally, it requires an understanding of the nature and dynamics of resources – how they work together to produce the outcomes of healthcare.

Reference

1   Kaplan R and Norton D (1996) *Using the Balanced Scorecard as a Strategic Management System.* Harvard Business Review, Boston, MA.

Bibliography

General

Deming WE (1943) *Statistical Adjustment of Data*. John Wiley & Sons, New York (republished in 1964 by Dover Publications Inc., New York).

Deming WE (1986) *Out of the Crisis*. Massachusetts Institute of Technology Centre for Advanced Engineering Study, Cambridge, MA.

Deming WE (1993) *The New Economics for Industry, Government and Education*. Massachusetts Institute of Technology Centre for Advanced Engineering Study, Cambridge, MA.

Feigenbaum AV (1983) *Total Quality Control* (3e). McGraw-Hill Book Company, New York.

Johnson G and Scholes K (1999) *Exploring Corporate Strategy* (5e). Prentice Hall International (UK), London.

Juran JM (1988) *Juran on Planning for Quality*. The Free Press, New York.

Senge P (1990) *The Fifth Discipline: the art and practice of learning organisations*. Doubleday, New York.

Senge P (1999) *A Dance of Change*. Nicholas Brealey, London.

Shewart WA (1931) *Economic Control of Quality of Manufactured Product*. D Van Nostrand Company Inc., Princeton, NJ (republished in 1980 by the American Society for Control, Milwaukee, WI).

Shewart WA (1939) *Statistical Method for the Viewpoint of Quality Control*. Graduate School of the Department of Agriculture, Washington, DC (republished in 1989 by Dover Publications Inc., New York).

Workforce

NHS Executive (2000) *The Vital Connection: an equalities framework for the NHS*. NHS Executive, Leeds;
www.doh.gov.uk/nhsequalitysframework.htm

NHS Executive (1999) *Working Together: securing a quality workforce for the NHS*. NHS Executive, Leeds; www.open.gov.newnhs/hstrat.htm

NHS Executive (2000) *Improving Working Lives*. NHS Executive, Leeds; www.doh.gov.uk/iwl

NHS Executive (2000) *Positively Diverse: Report 2000*. NHS Executive, Leeds; www.positivelydiverse.org.uk

Estate and supplies

Merry PM (ed.) (2000) *Wellards NHS Handbook 2000–01*. JMH Publishing, London.

NHS Estates (1999) *Developing an NHS Estate Strategy*. The Stationery Office, London.

NHS Estates (2001) *Building Better Healthcare*. Presentation Portfolio, CD. The Stationery Office, London.

NHS Executive (2000) *Capital Investment Manual*. The Stationery Office, London.

NHS Executive (2000) *Concode*. The Stationery Office, London.

NHS Executive (2000) *Estatecode*. The Stationery Office, London.

NHS Executive (2000) *Firecode*. The Stationery Office, London.

HSC 1999/143. *Review of NHS Procurement: Implementing the Recommendations*. Department of Health, London.

NHS Purchasing and Supply Agency; www.pasa.doh.gov.uk

NHS Logistics Authority; www.logistics.nhs.uk

Finance

Exposition Handbook; www.doh.gov.uk/allocations

Department of Health (2000) *Departmental Report: The Government plans*. Department of Health, London; www.doh.gov.uk/dohreport/report2000

Convisor R, Retondo M and Loveless M (1995) *Universal Health Coverage, Rationing and HIV Care: lessons from the Oregon Health Plan Medicaid Reform*. Self-published.

Nord E (1999) *Cost Value Analysis in Health Care: make sense out of QALYs*. Cambridge University Press, Cambridge.

Crick S (2000) *The Burden and Use of DALYs in Planning Healthcare Services*. NHS Executive, Eastern Region, Cambridge.

Jones T and Prowle M (1987) *Health Service Finance: an introduction*. The Certified Accountants Educational Trust, London.

NHS (1999) *Public Private Partnerships in the NHS: the Private Finance Initiative*. The Stationery Office, London.

Quality, performance and statistical process control

Affourtit BB (1992) Statistical process control applied to software. In: GG Schulmeyer and JI McManus (eds) *Total Quality Management for Software*. Van Nostrand Reinhold, New York.

Burr IW (1976) *Statistical Quality Control Methods.* Marcel Dekker Inc., New York.

Grant EL and Leavenworth RS (1988) *Statistical Quality Control* (6e). McGraw-Hill Book Company, New York.

Hotelling H (1947) Multivariate quality control, illustrated by the air testing of sample bombsites. In: E Churchill, MW Hastay and J Wallis (eds) *Selected Techniques of Statistical Analysis for Scientific and Industrial Research and Production and Management Engineering.* McGraw-Hill Book Company, New York.

Montgomery DC (1985) *Introduction to Statistical Quality Control.* John Wiley & Sons, New York.

Wheeler DJ and Chambers DS (1992) *Understanding Statistical Process Control* (2e). SPC Press, Knoxville, TN.

Munoz J and Nielson C (1991) SPC: what data should I collect? What charts should I use? *Qual Progress.* **24**: 50–2.

American Society for Quality; www.asq.org

Commission for Health Improvement (CHI); www.chi.nhs.uk

Institute for Health Improvement; www.ihi.org

National Institute for Clinical Excellence (NICE); www.nice.org.uk

Box G and Luceno A (1997) *Statistical Control by Monitoring Feedback Adjustment.* Wiley, New Jersey; http://catelog2.wiley.com/catelog

Healthcare

The NHS Plan: a plan for investment; a plan for action. Presented to Parliament by the Secretary of State for Health By Command of Her Majesty, July 2000; www.doh.gov.uk/nhsplan/contentspdf.htm

NHS Direct; www.nhsdirect.nhs.uk

National electronic Library for Health; www.nelh.nhs.uk

Information management

Bullas S (1994) *Managing Hospital Quality and Cost: using patient-based information.* Longman, London.

Project management

PRINCE II. Office of Government and Commerce (formerly CCTA); www.ogc.gov.uk/prince

Simulation

www.pqsystems.com, www.qa-inc.com, www.minitab.com, www.sas.com, www.spss.com, www.statsoft.com

Risk and benefit review

www.palisade.com

Statistical techniques

Burr JT (1990) The tools of quality. Part VI. Pareto charts. *Qual Progress.* 23: 59–61.

Burr JT (1990) The tools of quality. Part VII. Scatter diagrams. *Qual Progress.* 23: 87–9.

Nolan KM (1990) Planning a control chart. *Qual Progress.* 23: 51–5.

Sarazen JS (1990) The tools of quality. Part II. Cause and effect diagrams. *Qual Progress.* 23: 59–62.

Shainin PD (1990) The tools of quality. Part IV. Histograms. *Qual Progress.* 23: 75–8.

Appendix 1   Business case

Outline

Introduction
Summary
Concept
Patient care and service benefits
Project description
Options
Capital and revenue costs
Financing and procurement arrangements
Project management arrangements
Action plan
Appendices

Benefits checklist

Benefits categories

- Effectiveness
- Efficiency
- Economy
- Accessibility
- Risk reduction
- Satisfaction

Checklist of benefits

1 Improved quality of:
   - care and treatment of patients
   - patient satisfaction
   - administrative processes
   - business processes
   - information provided to external organisations (e.g. GPs, purchasers).
2 Avoiding duplication of effort:
   - writing data (e.g. patient's name and address)
   - asking patients the same questions many times

- inputting data into systems
- by providing management information as a by-product of operational processes.
3 Improved processes by simplifying, reducing, speeding, etc.:
  - clinical
  - administrative
  - management.
4 Reduced risk:
  - complications and adverse reactions
  - litigation
  - technology.
5 Availability of accurate, up-to-date information to communicate to:
  - patients
  - relatives and friends
  - colleagues
  - staff
  - GPs
  - purchasers
  - others.
6 Improved planning and forecasting.
7 Improved control or co-ordination.
8 Improved organisation of resources:
  - staff time and skills
  - use of buildings and equipment.
9 Avoiding overheads:
  - staffing
  - accommodation.
10 Avoiding need for paper or other consumables.
11 Reducing costs of:
  - care and treatment processes
  - administrative processes
  - management processes
  - maintaining or managing information systems.
12 Improved security.
13 Provision of more useful information to support clinical and management processes.
14 Ability to meet legal or other statutory requirements:
  - Patient's Charter
  - Health and Safety

- demands for information.

Risks checklist

Category	Sub-category
Process risks	Systems do not support required processes Process development shortcomings Service more complex than existing processes
Management control	Project management Adjustment of management systems
Performance risks	Response times (applications) Support (quality and response time) Maintenance (hardware/software, quality/response) Training (quality and response time)
Availability risks	Completion delays Failure and breakdown
Demand risks	Service under-utilised Service over-utilised Functions not required due to changes
Functionality risks	System does not do what is expected
Cost overruns	Supplier and customer
User issues	Failure to gain commitment System not used as intended Inadequate user interface
Obsolescence	New technology renders existing system obsolete Supplier fails to invest in development
Integration issues	Failure to develop interfaces Interfaces do not work as intended
Ownership	Cost of ownership Failure to establish sense of ownership
Failure to achieve expected benefits	Failure to obtain cash from cash-releasing benefits Failure to obtain quality improvements and other non-cash-releasing benefits
Needs identification	Under-specifying Over-specifying
Needs communication	True reflection of needs in procurement documentation Misunderstanding of needs by supplier
Contract issues	Risk of opportunism Failure to balance for hidden information and hidden actions Failure to provide incentives for supplier and customer to conform to contract Failure to agree variations
Litigation	Failure to conform to legal requirements Legal issues regarding clinical use of patient information
Legislation	New legislation leads to change in requirement

Appendix 2 Clinical outcome indicators

1 Pregnancy under the age of 16 years
2 Therapeutic abortion rates
3 Childhood incidence of measles
4 Cervical cancer mortality
5 Suicide rate
6 Rate of emergency admission for diabetic ketoacidosis
7 Longer inpatient stays for children with asthma
8 30-day survival after admission for fractured neck of femur
9 Discharge home within 56 days of admission with hip fracture
10 30-day survival after admission for myocardial infarction
11 Re-operation within 1 year of transurethral prostatectomy
12   Emergency readmission within 28 days of discharge from medical specialty
13 30-day survival after admission for stroke
14 Discharge home within 56 days of admission for stroke
15 Psychiatric inpatients: death within 1 year of discharge
16 Psychiatric inpatients aged $\geqslant 65$ years: death within 1 year of discharge
17 Psychiatric inpatients: suicide within 1 year of discharge
18 Proportion of first births by Caesarean section
19 Vaginal delivery after Caesarean section
20 Babies admitted to a neonatal unit
21 28-day emergency readmission: removal of tonsils/adenoids
22 D&C rates in women under 40 years
23 Use of medical methods for early termination of pregnancy
24 Survival with cancer of the trachea, bronchus and lung
25 Survival with cancer of the large bowel
26 Breast cancer
27 Survival with cancer of the ovary
28 28-day emergency readmission: elective operation for cataract
29 28-day emergency readmission: emergency appendectomy
30 28-day emergency readmission: elective prostatectomy
31 28-day emergency readmission: elective hysterectomy
32 28-day emergency readmission: elective total hip replacement
33 Survival with cancer of the stomach
34 Survival with cancer of the cervix uteri
35 Cardiac procedures – standardised procedure ratios for coronary angiography, angioplasty and coronary artery bypass graft
36 Breastfeeding
37 Smoking during pregnancy
38 Registration with general dental practitioner
39 Decayed, missing and filled teeth in children aged 5 years
40 Colorectal cancer
41 Emergency admissions

Appendix 3   Electronic patient records

Level 6	**Advanced multi-media and telematics** Level 5 plus Telemedicine, other multi-media applications (e.g. picture archiving and communications systems)
Level 5	**Specialty-specific support** Level 4 plus Special clinical modules, document imaging
Level 4	**Clinical knowledge and decision support** Level 3 plus Electronic access to knowledge bases, embedded guidelines, rules, electronic alerts, expert system support
Level 3	**Clinical activity support** Level 2 plus Electronic clinical orders, results reporting, prescribing, multiprofessional care pathways
Level 2	**Integrated clinical diagnosis and treatment support** Level 1 plus Integrated master patient index, departmental systems
Level 1	**Clinical administrative data** Patient administration and independent departmental systems

Source: NHS Executive (1998) *Information for Health*. NHS Executive, Leeds.

Index

Page numbers in *italics* refer to figures and tables.

accountability 86, 154
ad hoc exercises vs. continuous monitoring
    14–15
administrative process 130
    change, example 132–5
adverse events
    clinical governance initiative 86, 87
    see also medical errors
advertising, for staff 29
annual performance planning cycle 152–3
annual staff-attitude survey 33–4
audit 7
    statistical 118–23
    topic 116–18

benchmarking
    definition 148
    external comparisons 52, 94, 158, *159,*
        160
    internal service comparisons 158, *160*
benefits checklist, business case example
    177–8
best practice, definition 149
'blame culture' 170
budget flexibility 81
budget reporting 79–80
budgeting 73–5
    approaches 75–7
    clinical 77–9
    management 7, *14,* 107, 123–4
bullying and harassment 19
business cases 81–2
    example 177–9
business planning process 7, 81–3

Cabinet Office Review 53
Cancer Services Collaborative 137–9
capital allocations 67–8
    business planning 81–3
Capital Equipping Manager 52
Capital Investment Manual 39
Capital Replacement Programme 52

capital spending, planned NHS 68
case-mix groups 107–16
    and clinical outcomes 112–14
    framework 111–12
    measures 109
    and resource management 109, 111, 116
    and resource use, variations in 115
    UK experience 109–12
    US experience 108–9
Case-mix Management System 78, 94, 109
    principles 109–11
CASPE 77, 111
change
    demographic 22
    drivers 10–13, 63–4, 75
    examples 132–42
    future for 142–3
    key concepts 129–32
    making space for 168–9
    process *see* process change
clinical audit *see* audit
clinical budgeting 77–9
clinical directorate structure 77–8
clinical governance 7, *14,* 86–9
Clinical and Health Outcomes Knowledge
    Base 114
clinical outcomes
    case-mix groups and 112–14
    indicators 113–14, 181
clinical process 130
comparisons between organisations
    benchmarking 52, 94, 158, *159, 160*
    mortality ratios 120–1
    performance measures 158, *160,* 161–2
    see also under cost
computerisation
    financial systems 52
    GP practices 87, 88, 156
    see also electronic patient records (EPRs)
Concode 39
condition–treatment pairs 70–1
consultant appraisal 160, *161*

continuous monitoring vs. ad hoc exercises 14–15
continuous quality improvement, length-of-stay 123
cost
    comparisons between organisations 94, 95, 96–7
        HRGs 98, 99–100, *101*, 103, 112
    efficiency and 103–7
    of poor quality care 89
    and quality 88–9
        double feedback loop 116, *117*
    of waste *90*, 105
    see also reference costs
cost drivers, definition 96
cost of living, staff recruitment 24–5
cost minimisation, definition 148
cost pool, definition 96
costing 92–7
    definitions 95–6
    methods
        bottom-up 97, 104
        top-down 94–5, 96, 104
    principles 94
    use of EPRs 97, 100
critical care, reference costs *102*
critical mass standard *159*
Crossman formula, financial allocation 64
cultural (whole system) change, example 140–2
culture of organisation 170–1

DALYs *see* disability-adjusted life years
decision timing, budgeting 74–5
decision-making behaviour 8–10
    changing 11–12
    political pressure vs. rational 4–5
demographic change, staff recruitment 22
Department for Education and Employment (DfEE) 30–1
Department of Health
    CASPE 77, 111
    clinical governance initiative 86–7
    cost and quality management 106–7
    expenditure plans 67–8
    NHS *Costing Manual* 92–4, 95
    performance assessment data 162
deployment of resources 6, 7
diagnostic related groups (DRGs) 108–9, *110*, 111

direct costs, definition 95–6
disability-adjusted life years (DALYs) 72–3
diversity in the workforce 25–8

effectiveness
    definition 149
    in use of information 13–16
effects analysis, failure modes and 129
efficacy, definition 149
efficiency
    and cost 103–7
    definition 149
    in use of information 13–16
EFQM *see* European Foundation Quality Management Excellence Model
elective inpatients, reference costs *101*
electronic patient records (EPRs)
    committing project resources *6*
    levels 183
    national information strategy 87, 88
    performance measures 156
    use in costing 97, 100
energy performance, estates 47
equal opportunities objectives *27*
ERIC *see* Estates Returns Information Collection
Estatecode 39
estate(s)
    EU Procurement Rules 57–9
    and facilities 38–9
    performance management
        future of 59
        organisational level 40–2
        philosophy 38–9
        strategy 40
        example 42–9
Estates Returns Information Collection (ERIC) 41–2
ethnic minorities (staff recruitment) 25, 26
    profile *27, 28*
        internal benchmarking 158, *160*
European Foundation Quality Management (EFQM) Excellence Model 38–9
European funding comparisons 63
European Union (EU) Procurement Rules 57–9
evaluation, definition 149
evidence-based approach 1, 2, 171
exception reporting 15–16
exit interviews 34

expenditure control 74

facilities *see* estate(s), and facilities
failure modes and effects analysis 129
failure rates 128–9
family-friendly working practices 31
final outcome, definition 148
finance
  control within organisations 73–83
  international comparisons 63
  rationing 69–73
  sources 61–3
financial allocations 63–9, 74
  capital 67–8, 81–3
  case-mix information 112
  revenue 66–7
financial analysis, five-facet (estate) survey
  47
financial appraisal, business planning process
  82
financial computer systems 52
Firecode 39
fixed costs, definition 96
flexible working 29, 30–2
focus groups, NHS Plan Consultation 69
functional suitability, estates 44

general practitioners (GPs)
  computerisation of practices 87, 88, 156
  fundholding 65–6
  and practice staff *19*
  statistical audit 119–20
  see also primary care
'gold standard', performance measurement
  158, *159*
guidelines and protocols 91–2

harassment and bullying 19
hard vs. soft information 8–9
Health Action Zones 68, *69*
health authorities
  cost and quality management 106–7
  revenue allocations 66–7
health benefit groups (HBGs) 112
Health Improvement Programmes (HImPs)
  DALYs 73
  performance measures 152
  telemedicine and telecare options 87
healthcare resource groups (HRGs)
  case-mix information 111, 112

cost comparisons 98, 99–100, *101*, 103,
  112
individual consultant appraisal *161*
housing costs, staff recruitment *25*
Human Resources Performance
  Framework 33

improved patient outcomes/treatment,
  examples 132–9
Improving Working Lives 20–1
incremental budgets 75–6
indirect costs, definition 96
information averse vs. information seeking
  behaviour 9–10
Information for Health 87–8
Institute of Health Sciences, University of
  Oxford 114
integration
  of information and management 5–7
  strategic approach 169
intermediate outcome, definition 148
internal performance measures, ethnic
  minority composition of workforce
  158, *160*
internal service comparisons 158

land sales 62, 67
length-of-stay
  distribution 121–2
  reduction 123
lifesaving procedures, Oregon Rationing
  Plan 71
local authorities 22, *23–4*
  see also health authorities
local employment profile, staff recruitment
  23–4
local population information 22, 112
London School of Hygiene and Tropical
  Medicine 111, 114

management budgeting 7, *14*, 107, 123–4
management case, business planning process
  82
MBTI *see* Myers–Briggs Type Indicator
Medical Equipment Group 52
medical errors
  cost of *90*
  prospective information 91
  retrospective information 92
  see also adverse events

modernisation *see* change
monitoring
   ad hoc exercises vs. continuous 14–15
   definition 149
   'near misses' 134–5
   see also performance measurement
Myers–Briggs Type Indicator (MBTI) 8–9

National Audit Office 103–4
National Casemix Office 111–12
National Centre for Health Outcomes
   Development (NCHOD) 114
National electronic Library for Health
   (NeLH) 87, 88, 91
National Health Service *see* NHS
National Institute for Clinical Excellence
   (NICE) 91
National Insurance contributions 62
National Lotteries Act 63
National Performance Framework 107
National Schedule for Reference Costs 98,
   104
National Service Frameworks 91
National Statistics 22
nature of information 8–10
'near misses', monitoring 134–5
New Opportunities Fund 63
NHS
   cf. private-for-profit industries 142–3
   cost and quality management 106
   early performance indicators 146
   performance objectives 150–4
   resource allocation principles 64
   staffing statistics 18, 19
NHS census 69, 70
NHS and Community Care Act (1990)
   65–6
NHS *Costing Manual* 92–4, 95
NHS *Direct* 87
NHS Estates 37, 38–9, 40, 41, 59, *60*
NHS Executive
   Director of Finance 104
   family-friendly working practices 31
   Information for Health 87–8
   intervention to rectify poor performance
   107
   Resource Management Initiative 77–8,
   109, 111
   Working Together 20
NHS Logistics Authority 37, 50

NHS Performance Ratings 167
NHS Plan 20–1, 39
   Consultation 69–70
NHS Purchasing and Supply Agency 37,
   49–50, 59, *60*
NHS standards 91
NHS*net* 87, 114
nursing practice, RCN guidelines 92

Official Journal of the European Communities
   (*OJEC*) 58
operational objective, definition 148
optimal performance 6, 7
optional appraisal, business planning process
   81
Oregon Rationing Plan 70–1
organisational culture 170–1
outcomes
   clinical 112–14, 181
   improved patient, examples 135–9
   performance management 148
output, definition 148
overheads, definition 96

PACTs *see* planning agreements, clinical
   teams
Patient Administration Systems (PAS) 94,
   156
patient(s)
   -based information systems 109, 115
   expectations 4
   improved outcomes/treatment, examples
   132–9
PCGs/PCTs *see under* primary care
PDCA model *see* Plan–Do–Check–Act
   model
Performance Assessment Framework 151–2
Performance Fund 63
performance indicators *147*
   definition 148
   early NHS 146
   estates 47–8
   supplies *55*–7
performance management
   definitions 147–9
   future of 164
   see also under estate(s); supplies
performance measurement 7, 147
   development 145–7
   information sources 155–6

methods 156–62
organisational diversity 25–6
see also monitoring
performance objectives 149–55
supplies 51–3, 54
performance, poor 107, 120
performance review 149, 162–4
performance sub-objectives 155
PFI see Private Finance Initiative
physical condition, estates 43–4
PIN see Prior Information Notice
Plan–Do–Check–Act (PDCA) model
138–9
planning agreements, clinical teams
(PACTs) 77
planning, budget 74
political pressure vs. rational decision-
making 4–5
poor performance 107, 120
Positively Diverse study 19, 25, 35
power distribution, budgeting 75
Prescription Pricing Authority 87
primary care
and acute care collaboration, example
137–9
groups (PCGs) 66, 106–7
trusts (PCTs) 66
see also general practitioners (GPs)
PRINCE II (Projects in a Controlled
Environment) 82
Prior Information Notice (PIN) 58
Private Finance Initiative (PFI) 39, 59, 62,
67, 82, 124
process
components 130, 131
definition 130
see also business planning process;
statistical process control
process change 12–13, 128–9
and design principles 130–2, 133
examples 132–42
Procurement Rules, EU 57–9
prospective vs. retrospective information
13–14
quality and cost 89–92
protocols and guidelines 91–2

quality assurance, length-of-stay reduction
123
quality and cost see cost, and quality

Quality of Well-Being (QWB) scale 71
quality-adjusted life years (QALYs) 71–2
quantitative performance measures 157–62

rational decision-making vs. political
pressure 4–5
rationing 69–73
RCN see Royal College of Nursing
reference costs 98–100
limitations of 100–3
National Schedule 98, 104
registration of professionals 32
research, definition 149
Resource Allocation Working Party (RAWP)
64–5, 120
Resource Management Initiative 77–8,
109, 111
retrospective information see prospective vs.
retrospective information
revenue allocations, health authorities 66–7
risks checklist, business case example 179
Road Traffic (NHS Charges) Act 63
Royal College of Nursing (RCN) 92

salary enhancements 24
Scottish Executive, clinical outcomes
indicators 113–14
selective information 6
self-rostering 31
semi-fixed (step) costs, definition 96
Service and Financial Framework (SaFF)
152, 153
service user organisations, NHS Plan
Consultation 70
Shipman (Harold) Investigation 119–20
soft vs. hard information 8–9
space utilisation, estates 44–6
staff
absenteeism 19, 20, 26
commitment to performance
improvement 163–4
confidence about expressing concerns 35
confidentiality of responses 34
diversity 25–8
flexible working 29, 30–2
involvement 140–2, 154
most valued and valuable resource 19–21,
170
NHS cf. private-for-profit industries
142–3

staff (*cont.*):
  reduction, as cost-cutting measure 105
  salary enhancements 24
  self-rostering 31
  sickness 19, 20, 26
  structure of workforce 18–19
  views 33–5
staff recruitment 28–9
  competition with other employers 21–5
  cost of living 24–5
  cost of 30
  demographic change 22
  financial allocations 64
  local employment 23–4
  see also ethnic minorities (staff
      recruitment)
staff training 32–3
staff turnover levels 28–9
  high 19, 20, 26
  unavoidable and avoidable 34
stakeholders 3
standard, definition 148
standard gamble, QALYs 72
standardised mortality ratios 120–1
statistical audit 118–23
statistical process control 107, 129
statutory standards, estates 46–7
strategic case, business planning process 81
strategic objective, definition 148
styles of information use 8–10
supplies 49
  EU Procurement Rules 57–9
  performance indicators and measures
      55–7
  performance management
      future of 59
      organisational level 50–1

performance objectives 51–3, *54*
  strategy 49–53, *54*
surveys 155–6
  definition 149
  five-facet (estate) 47
  staff-attitude 33–4

target, definition 148
telemedicine and telecare 87
time management 169
time series analysis 157
time trade-off, QALYs 71
topic audit 116–18
Trust Financial Proformas (TFPs) 41

UK Clearing House on Health Outcomes
    113
University of London, outcomes
    information 114
USA, case-mix groups 108–9

'value-added' performance measures 160
variable costs, definition 96
variations in resource use 115

waiting-lists *12, 157, 158*
weighted capitation approach, revenue
    allocation 66, 67
whole-system (cultural) change, example
    140–2
Work Life Balance Case Studies (DfEE) 301
workforce *see* staff
working environment 29–32
Working Together 20
workshops, NHS Plan Consultation 69

zero-based budgets 76–7